NCEES
advancing licensure for engineers and surveyors

FE

other
disciplines
practice exam

978-1-932613-86-5

ISBN 978-1-932613-86-5

Printed in the United States of America
1st printing March 2017

CONTENTS

About NCEES

NCEES is a nonprofit organization made up of the U.S. engineering and surveying licensing boards in all 50 states, U.S. territories, and the District of Columbia. We develop and score the exams used for engineering and surveying licensure in the United States. NCEES also promotes professional mobility through its services for licensees and its member boards.

Engineering licensure in the United States is regulated by licensing boards in each state and territory. These boards set and maintain the standards that protect the public they serve. As a result, licensing requirements and procedures vary by jurisdiction, so stay in touch with your board (ncees.org/licensing-boards).

Exam Format

The FE exam contains 110 questions and is administered year-round via computer at approved Pearson VUE test centers. A 6-hour appointment time includes a tutorial, the exam, and a break. You'll have 5 hours and 20 minutes to complete the actual exam.

Beginning July 1, 2017, in addition to traditional multiple-choice questions with one correct answer, the FE exam will use common alternative item types such as

- Multiple correct options—allows multiple choices to be correct
- Point and click—requires examinees to click on part of a graphic to answer
- Drag and drop—requires examinees to click on and drag items to match, sort, rank, or label
- Fill in the blank—provides a space for examinees to enter a response to the question

To familiarize yourself with the format, style, and navigation of a computer-based exam, view the demo on ncees.org/ExamPrep.

Examinee Guide

The *NCEES Examinee Guide* is the official guide to policies and procedures for all NCEES exams. During exam registration and again on exam day, examinees must agree to abide by the conditions in the *Examinee Guide*, which includes the CBT Examinee Rules and Agreement. You can download the *Examinee Guide* at ncees.org/exams. It is your responsibility to make sure you have the current version.

Scoring and reporting

Exam results for computer-based exams are typically available 7–10 days after you take the exam. You will receive an email notification from NCEES with instructions to view your results in your MyNCEES account. All results are reported as pass or fail.

Updates on exam content and procedures

Visit us at **ncees.org/exams** for updates on everything exam-related, including specifications, exam-day policies, scoring, and corrections to published exam preparation materials. This is also where you will register for the exam and find additional steps you should follow in your state to be approved for the exam.

- The FE exam is a computer-based test (CBT). It is closed book with an electronic reference.

- Examinees have 6 hours to complete the exam, which contains 110 multiple-choice questions. The 6-hour time also includes a tutorial and an optional scheduled break.

- The FE exam uses both the International System of Units (SI) and the U.S. Customary System (USCS).

Knowledge	Number of Questions
1. **Mathematics and Advanced Engineering Mathematics**	12–18

    A. Analytic geometry and trigonometry
    B. Calculus
    C. Differential equations (e.g., homogeneous, nonhomogeneous, Laplace transforms)
    D. Numerical methods (e.g., algebraic equations, roots of equations, approximations, precision limits)
    E. Linear algebra (e.g., matrix operations)

2. Probability and Statistics   6–9

    A. Measures of central tendencies and dispersions (e.g., mean, mode, variance, standard deviation)
    B. Probability distributions (e.g., discrete, continuous, normal, binomial)
    C. Estimation (e.g., point, confidence intervals)
    D. Expected value (weighted average) in decision making
    E. Sample distributions and sizes
    F. Goodness of fit (e.g., correlation coefficient, least squares)

3. Chemistry   7–11

    A. Periodic table (e.g., nomenclature, metals and nonmetals, atomic structure of matter)
    B. Oxidation and reduction
    C. Acids and bases
    D. Equations (e.g., stoichiometry, equilibrium)
    E. Gas laws (e.g., Boyle's and Charles' Laws, molar volume)

4. Instrumentation and Data Acquisition   4–6

    A. Sensors (e.g., temperature, pressure, motion, pH, chemical constituents)
    B. Data acquisition (e.g., logging, sampling rate, sampling range, filtering, amplification, signal interface)
    C. Data processing (e.g., flow charts, loops, branches)

5. **Ethics and Professional Practice**   3–5
   A. Codes of ethics
   B. NCEES *Model Law* and *Model Rules*
   C. Public protection issues (e.g., licensing boards)

6. **Safety, Health, and Environment**   4–6
   A. Industrial hygiene (e.g., carcinogens, toxicology, MSDS, lower
      exposure limits)
   B. Basic safety equipment (e.g., pressure relief valves, emergency
      shut-offs, fire prevention and control, personal protective equipment)
   C. Gas detection and monitoring (e.g., O_2, CO, CO_2, CH_4, H_2S, Radon)
   D. Electrical safety

7. **Engineering Economics**   7–11
   A. Time value of money (e.g., present worth, annual worth, future worth,
      rate of return)
   B. Cost (e.g., incremental, average, sunk, estimating)
   C. Economic analyses (e.g., breakeven, benefit-cost, optimal economic life)
   D. Uncertainty (e.g., expected value and risk)
   E. Project selection (e.g., comparison of unequal life projects,
      lease/buy/make, depreciation, discounted cash flow)

8. **Statics**   8–12
   A. Resultants of force systems and vector analysis
   B. Concurrent force systems
   C. Force couple systems
   D. Equilibrium of rigid bodies
   E. Frames and trusses
   F. Area properties (e.g., centroids, moments of inertia, radius of gyration)
   G. Static friction

9. **Dynamics**   7–11
   A. Kinematics
   B. Linear motion (e.g., force, mass, acceleration)
   C. Angular motion (e.g., torque, inertia, acceleration)
   D. Mass moment of inertia
   E. Impulse and momentum (linear and angular)
   F. Work, energy, and power
   G. Dynamic friction
   H. Vibrations

10. **Strength of Materials**   8–12
    A. Stress types (e.g., normal, shear, bending, torsion)
    B. Combined stresses
    C. Stress and strain caused by axial loads, bending loads, torsion, or shear
    D. Shear and moment diagrams
    E. Analysis of beams, trusses, frames, and columns
    F. Deflection and deformations (e.g., axial, bending, torsion)
    G. Elastic and plastic deformation
    H. Failure theory and analysis (e.g., static/dynamic, creep, fatigue, fracture, buckling)

11. **Materials Science**   6–9

    A. Physical, mechanical, chemical, and electrical properties of ferrous metals
    B. Physical, mechanical, chemical, and electrical properties of nonferrous metals
    C. Physical, mechanical, chemical, and electrical properties of engineered materials (e.g., polymers, concrete, composites)
    D. Corrosion mechanisms and control

12. **Fluid Mechanics and Dynamics of Liquids**   8–12
    A. Fluid properties (e.g., Newtonian, non-Newtonian)
    B. Dimensionless numbers (e.g., Reynolds number, Froude number)
    C. Laminar and turbulent flow
    D. Fluid statics
    E. Energy, impulse, and momentum equations (e.g., Bernoulli equation)
    F. Pipe flow and friction losses (e.g., pipes, valves, fittings, Darcy-Weisbach equation, Hazen-Williams equation)
    G. Open-channel flow (e.g., Manning equation, drag)
    H. Fluid transport systems (e.g., series and parallel operations)
    I. Flow measurement
    J. Turbomachinery (e.g., pumps, turbines)

13. **Fluid Mechanics and Dynamics of Gases**   4–6
    A. Fluid properties (e.g., ideal and non-ideal gases)
    B. Dimensionless numbers (e.g., Reynolds number, Mach number)
    C. Laminar and turbulent flow
    D. Fluid statics
    E. Energy, impulse, and momentum equations
    F. Duct and pipe flow and friction losses
    G. Fluid transport systems (e.g., series and parallel operations)
    H. Flow measurement
    I. Turbomachinery (e.g., fans, compressors, turbines)

14. **Electricity, Power, and Magnetism**   7–11
   A. Electrical fundamentals (e.g., charge, current, voltage, resistance, power, energy)
   B. Current and voltage laws (Kirchhoff, Ohm)
   C. DC circuits
   D. Equivalent circuits (series, parallel, Norton's theorem, Thevenin's theorem)
   E. Capacitance and inductance
   F. AC circuits (e.g., real and imaginary components, complex numbers, power factor, reactance and impedance)
   G. Measuring devices (e.g., voltmeter, ammeter, wattmeter)

15. **Heat, Mass, and Energy Transfer**   9–14

   A. Energy, heat, and work
   B. Thermodynamic laws (e.g., 1st law, 2nd law)
   C. Thermodynamic equilibrium
   D. Thermodynamic properties (e.g., entropy, enthalpy, heat capacity)
   E. Thermodynamic processes (e.g., isothermal, adiabatic, reversible, irreversible)
   F. Mixtures of nonreactive gases
   G. Heat transfer (e.g., conduction, convection, and radiation)
   H. Mass and energy balances
   I. Property and phase diagrams (e.g., T-s, P-h)
   J. Phase equilibrium and phase change
   K. Combustion and combustion products (e.g., CO, CO_2, NO_X, ash, particulates)
   L. Psychrometrics (e.g., relative humidity, wet-bulb)

1.   The equation of a sphere with center at $(0, 1, -2)$ and a radius of 9 is:

- ○ A. $x^2 + (y - 1)^2 + (z + 2)^2 = 81$
- ○ B. $x^2 + (y + 1)^2 + (z - 2)^2 = 81$
- ○ C. $(x + 1)^2 + (y + 1)^2 + (z + 2)^2 = 81$
- ○ D. $(x + 1)^2 + (y + 1)^2 + (z + 2)^2 = 9$

2.   Three lines are defined by the three equations:

$$x + y = 0$$
$$x - y = 0$$
$$2x + y = 1$$

The three lines form a triangle with vertices at:

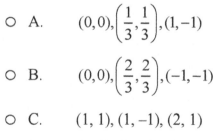

- ○ A. $(0,0), \left(\dfrac{1}{3}, \dfrac{1}{3}\right), (1, -1)$

- ○ B. $(0,0), \left(\dfrac{2}{3}, \dfrac{2}{3}\right), (-1, -1)$

- ○ C. $(1, 1), (1, -1), (2, 1)$
- ○ D. $(1, 1), (3, -3), (-2, -1)$

3. The indefinite integral of $x^3 - x + 1$ is:

    ○ A. $3x^2 - 1 + C$

    ○ B. $\dfrac{x^4}{3} - \dfrac{x^2}{2} + 1 + C$

    ○ C. $\dfrac{x^4}{3} - \dfrac{x^2}{2} + 1$

    ○ D. $\dfrac{x^4}{4} - \dfrac{x^2}{2} + x + C$

4. What is the area of the region in the first quadrant that is bounded by the line $y = 1$, the curve $x = y^{3/2}$, and the y-axis?

    ○ A.   2/5

    ○ B.   3/5

    ○ C.   2/3

    ○ D.   1

5.   The following equation describes a second-order system:

$$\frac{d^2y}{dt^2} + 6\frac{dy}{dt} + 25y = x(t)$$

The system may be described as:

○ A.   nonlinear
○ B.   overdamped
○ C.   critically damped
○ D.   underdamped

6.   Which of the following is the general solution to the differential equation and boundary condition shown below?

$$\frac{dy}{dt} + 5y = 0; \; y(0) = 1$$

○ A. e^{5t}
○ B. e^{-5t}
○ C. $e^{\sqrt{-5t}}$
○ D. $5e^{-5t}$

7. Suppose $f(t) = t^2$. The area under the curve for $0 \leq t \leq 2$, estimated by using the trapezoidal rule with $\Delta t = 0.5$, is most nearly:

- A. 4.00
- B. 2.75
- C. 2.67
- D. 1.33

8. The roots of $F = \dfrac{x^3 + 6x^2 + 11x + 6}{x + 1}$ are most nearly:

- A. $-1, -2, -3$
- B. $2, -3$
- C. $-2, -3$
- D. $2, 3$

9. The term $\dfrac{(1-i)^2}{(1+i)^2}$, where $i = \sqrt{-1}$, is most nearly:

- A. $1 + i$
- B. 0
- C. $-1 + i$
- D. -1

10.   Given the vectors $\mathbf{a} = (-2\mathbf{i} + 3\mathbf{j} + 4\mathbf{k})$ and $\mathbf{b} = (3\mathbf{i} + 2\mathbf{k})$, the cross product, $\mathbf{a} \times \mathbf{b}$, is most nearly:

- A. $6\mathbf{i} - 16\mathbf{j} - 9\mathbf{k}$
- B. $6\mathbf{i} + 16\mathbf{j} + 9\mathbf{k}$
- C. $-6\mathbf{i} - 16\mathbf{j} - 9\mathbf{k}$
- D. $6\mathbf{i} + 16\mathbf{j} - 9\mathbf{k}$

11.   Which of the following is a unit vector perpendicular to the plane determined by the vectors $\mathbf{A} = 2\mathbf{i} + 4\mathbf{j}$ and $\mathbf{B} = \mathbf{i} + \mathbf{j} - \mathbf{k}$?

- A. $-2\mathbf{i} + \mathbf{j} - \mathbf{k}$

- B. $\dfrac{1}{\sqrt{5}}(\mathbf{i} + 2\mathbf{j})$

- C. $\dfrac{1}{\sqrt{6}}(-2\mathbf{i} + \mathbf{j} - \mathbf{k})$

- D. $\dfrac{1}{\sqrt{6}}(-2\mathbf{i} - \mathbf{j} - \mathbf{k})$

12.   Consider the three vectors:

$$\mathbf{A} = 5\mathbf{i} - 3\mathbf{j} + 6\mathbf{k}$$
$$\mathbf{B} = -\mathbf{i} + 2\mathbf{j} + 2\mathbf{k}$$
$$\mathbf{C} = 2\mathbf{i} + 3\mathbf{j} - 4\mathbf{k}$$

The product $(\mathbf{B} \times \mathbf{C}) \cdot \mathbf{A}$ is most nearly:

- A. -112
- B.   0
- C.   28
- D.   112

13.   A series of measurements gave values of 11, 11, 11, 11, 12, 13, 13, 14, for which the arithmetic mean is 12. The population standard deviation is most nearly:

○ A.   1.42
○ B.   1.25
○ C.   1.19
○ D.   1.12

14.   You are testing the hypothesis that the mean sidewall strength of cans is greater than 150 psi. A sample of eight independent cans has been tested, and the mean breaking strength of the sample is 153 psi. Past experience has shown that the population standard deviation is 3 psi. The probability that the mean breaking strength is less than 150 psi is most nearly: .

○ A.   0.0026
○ B.   0.1587
○ C.   0.8413
○ D.   0.9974

15. You throw two 6-sided fair dice. The probability that the sum will be less than 12 is most nearly:

- ○ A. 0.028
- ○ B. 0.083
- ○ C. 0.333
- ○ D. 0.972

16. You have a fair coin that you toss ten times. The probability of getting exactly four heads in ten tosses is most nearly:

- ○ A. 0.1
- ○ B. 0.2
- ○ C. 0.4
- ○ D. 0.5

17.   You wish to estimate the mean M of a population from a sample of size n drawn from the population. For the sample, the mean is x and the standard deviation is s. The probable accuracy of the estimate improves with an increase in:

   ○ A. M
   ○ B. n
   ○ C. s
   ○ D. $M + s$

18.   A set consists of four points that have the following coordinates:

x	y
2.3	5.6
1.2	4.1
4.2	8.6
6.3	10.1

If linear least squares regression is used, the equation that best fits this data is:

   ○ A. $y = 2.9 + 1.2x$
   ○ B. $y = 2.7 + 1.2x$
   ○ C. $y = 2.9 - 1.2x$
   ○ D. $y = 2.5 + 1.4x$

                                 NEXT→

19.   The molecular (or atomic) weight (g/g-mole) of sulfuric acid (H_2SO_4) is most nearly:

○ A.   32
○ B.   49
○ C.   98
○ D.   116

20.   The element tin has eight different stable isotopes. The atomic nuclei of all eight isotopes contain how many protons?

_____

Answer to the nearest integer.

21.   The volume (L) of 1 mol of H_2O at 546 K and 1.00 atm pressure is most nearly:

○ A.   11.2
○ B.   14.9
○ C.   22.4
○ D.   44.8

22.   All of the following are oxidation-reduction reactions **except:**

    ○ A. $CaCO_3 \rightarrow CaO + CO_2$

    ○ B. $CO_2 + C \rightarrow 2CO$

    ○ C. $Fe + S \rightarrow FeS$

    ○ D. $2SO_2 + O_2 \rightarrow 2SO_3$

23.   The atomic weights of sodium, oxygen, and hydrogen are 23, 16, and 1, respectively. To neutralize 4 g of NaOH dissolved in 1 L of water requires 1 L of:

    ○ A.   0.001 normal HCl solution

    ○ B.   0.01 normal HCl solution

    ○ C.   0.1 normal HCl solution

    ○ D.   1.0 normal HCl solution

24.   Consider the following equation:

$$K = \frac{[C]^2[D]^2}{[A]^4[B]}$$

The equation above is the formulation of the chemical equilibrium constant equation for which of the following reactions?

    ○ A. $C_2 + D_2 \leftrightarrow A_4 + B$

    ○ B. $4A + B \leftrightarrow 2C + 2D$

    ○ C. $4C + 2D \leftrightarrow 2A + B$

    ○ D. $A_4 + B \leftrightarrow C_2 + D_2$

25. Match the numbers with the correct blanks in the equation to balance the reaction. Some numbers may be used more than once.

_____ CH_4 _____ $O_2 \rightarrow$ _____ $CO_2 +$ _____ H_2O

<u>1</u>   <u>2</u>   <u>3</u>   <u>4</u>

26. The pressure of 100 kg of nitrogen (N_2) at 70°C in a 100-m³ tank is most nearly:

   ○ A.   2,850 kPa
   ○ B.   102 kPa
   ○ C.   20 kPa
   ○ D.   102 mPa

27.   A resistance temperature detector (RTD) provides a resistance output that is related to temperature. Consider an RTD with $R_o = 100 \ \Omega$, $\alpha = 0.004°C^{-1}$, and $T_o = 0°C$. The change in resistance (Ω) of the RTD for a 10°C change in temperature is most nearly:

       ○ A.   0.04
       ○ B.   0.4
       ○ C.   4.0
       ○ D.   100.4

28.   Water flow rate in a pipe is measured using a 5-minute time interval. The flow rate data is plotted versus time, and a smooth curve is passed through the data points. The total volume passing the measuring point over a 24-hour period can be estimated as the:

       ○ A.   highest point on the flow vs. time curve

       ○ B.   average of all flows measured

       ○ C.   area under the flow vs. time curve

       ○ D.   slope of the tangent to the steepest portion of the flow vs. time curve

29. The continuous harmonic data signal is given below:

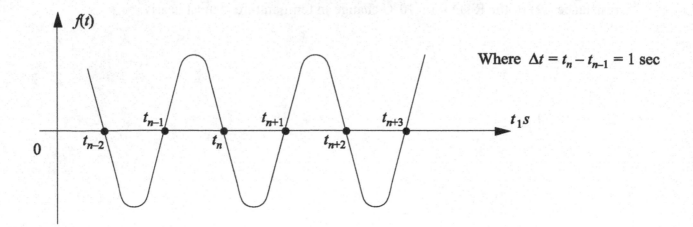

Where $\Delta t = t_n - t_{n-1} = 1$ sec

The minimum sample frequency f_s required to properly reconstruct the continuous signal is:

- ○ A. 1 sample per 4 sec
- ○ B. 1 sample per 2 sec
- ○ C. 1 sample per 1 sec
- ○ D. 2 samples per 1 sec

NEXT→

30. The following segment of pseudocode describes a segment of a computer program:

> Set A = 17
> Set K = 2
> While K ≤ 4
>   A = A/K
>   K = K + 1
> End While
> Print A

The value of A that is printed is most nearly:

- ○ A.   0.71
- ○ B.   2.83
- ○ C.   4.25
- ○ D.   408

31. Your bachelor of science program in electrical engineering was mostly concentrated in electronics and computer engineering courses. When you are ready to graduate, the computer and electronics industry is in a terrible slump, but the electrical power industry is booming. Ethically, you can:

- ○ A.   develop a three-sentence paragraph addition to your resume describing how your academic background is applicable to the power industry

- ○ B.   rework your resume to point out all the seminar-like discussions you have had with friends who studied electrical power courses

- ○ C.   add to your resume the summer job spent wiring houses for your uncle as "residential electrical power systems internship"

- ○ D.   purchase a transcript from a mail-order university with an electrical power emphasis

32.   As a professional engineer originally licensed 30 years ago, you are asked to evaluate a newly developed computerized control system for a public transportation system. The owner requires a currently licensed engineer to evaluate the system. You may accept this project if:

    ○ A.   you are competent in the area of modern control systems

    ○ B.   your professional engineering license has lapsed, but you have two FE interns working for you

    ○ C.   you took a transportation course in college

    ○ D.   you have regularly attended meetings of a professional engineering society

33.   A person who has a license as a professional engineer, known as a licensee, has obligations to the following:

Select **all** that apply.

    ☐ A.   other persons who have licenses as professional engineers

    ☐ B.   the court system

    ☐ C.   the public

    ☐ D.   the employer of the licensee

    ☐ E.   the clients of the licensee/licensee's employer

    ☐ F.   the licensee's alma mater

34. Violations of the Rules of Professional Conduct should be reported to the:

- ○ A. local chapter of the professional engineers association in the county and state in which the violation occurred
- ○ B. state chapter of the professional engineers association in the state in which the violation occurred
- ○ C. office of the attorney in the county and state in which the violation occurred
- ○ D. board of registration in the state in which the violation occurred

35. Which of the compounds listed below has the lowest lethal dose, based on LD_{50}, where the LD_{50} is based on oral or skin exposure by test animals?

- ○ A. Phenobarbital
- ○ B. Strychnine
- ○ C. Nicotine
- ○ D. PCBs

36. Basic safety equipment for a university chemistry laboratory class includes all of the following **except:**

- ○ A. fire extinguisher
- ○ B. safety goggles
- ○ C. splash apron
- ○ D. steel-toed boots

37. Benzene (molecular weight 78) is a constituent of gasoline used in automobiles and is a hazardous material. The limit for the ambient atmosphere is 1 ppm by volume. When a gas tank is filled, the vapor in the tank is vented into the atmosphere unless a vapor recovery system is used.

    If 100 g of benzene were emitted to the atmosphere, then the volume (m^3) of air outside the tank that would be uniformly contaminated to the level of 1.0 ppm would be most nearly:

    - ○ A. 31×10^6
    - ○ B. 31×10^5
    - ○ C. 31×10^3
    - ○ D. 31×10^2

38. Portable electric tools are frequently used where operators may encounter water or other conductive materials. The safety device required by *The National Electrical Code* to protect against accidental electrocution in wet/damp environments is known as a:

    - ○ A. ground rod
    - ○ B. properly sized circuit breaker
    - ○ C. ground fault interrupter (GFI)
    - ○ D. two-conductor power cord

39.   A project has the estimated cash flows shown below.

Year End	0	1	2	3	4
Cash Flow	–$1,100	–$400	+$1,000	+$1,000	+$1,000

Using an interest rate of 12% per year compounded annually, the annual worth of the project is most nearly:

- A. $450
- B. $361
- C. $320
- D. $226

40.   A new sander costs $3,600 and has an annual maintenance cost of $400. Salvage value after 7 years is $600. If the interest rate is 10%, the present worth is most nearly:

- A.   –$1,640
- B.   –$3,290
- C.   –$3,600
- D.   –$5,240

41. Which of the following situations is most appropriate for using break-even analysis?

○ A.   Calculating the interest rate that will ensure that costs and returns are equal

○ B.   Determining the number of units to produce to ensure that income covers expenses

○ C.   Establishing the minimum return on an investment over a set number of years

○ D.   Forecasting the amount of product that must be produced to meet a set profit margin

42. A company can manufacture a product using hand tools. Tools will cost $1,000, and the manufacturing cost per unit will be $1.50. As an alternative, an automated system will cost $15,000 with a manufacturing cost per unit of $0.50. If the anticipated annual volume is 5,000 units and interest is neglected, the payback period (yr) to buy the automated system rather than the hand tool method is most nearly:

○ A.   2.8

○ B.   3.6

○ C.   15.0

○ D.   never

43. A company is planning to manufacture a product and sell it for $2.00 per unit. The following data apply:

Cost of the equipment to manufacture the product = $200,000
Net salvage value of equipment at the end of its estimated economic life of 10 years = $10,000
Number of units per year the equipment can manufacture = 1,000,000
Direct labor costs per unit = $0.30
Direct material costs per unit = $0.65
Variable administrative and selling expenses per unit = $0.20
Fixed overhead costs per year (not including depreciation) = $150,000

Demand Units/Year	Probability
500,000	0.1
600,000	0.2
700,000	0.4
800,000	0.2
900,000	0.1

If the demand follows the probability distribution shown in the table and straight-line depreciation is used, the expected average net profit per year before taxes is most nearly:

- A. $445,000
- B. $426,000
- C. $226,000
- D. $45,000

44. You must choose between four pieces of comparable equipment based on the cash flows given below. All four pieces have a life of 8 yr.

Parameter	Equipment			
	A	B	C	D
First cost	$25,000	$35,000	$20,000	$40,000
Annual costs	$8,000	$6,000	$9,000	$5,000
Salvage value	$2,500	$3,500	$2,000	$4,000

The discount rate is 12%. Ignore taxes. The two most preferable projects and the difference between their present worth values are most nearly:

○ A.   A and C, $234

○ B.   B and D, $234

○ C.   A and C, $170

○ D.   B and D, $170

45. The magnitude (N) of the resultant of the three coplanar forces, A, B, and C, is most nearly:

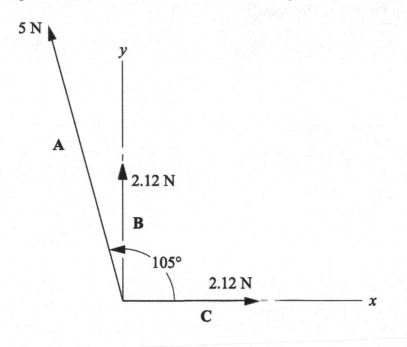

- ○ A. 7.0
- ○ B. 7.8
- ○ C. 9.2
- ○ D. 10.3

46. A cylinder weighing 120 N rests between two frictionless walls as shown in the figure below. The wall reaction (N) at Point A is most nearly:

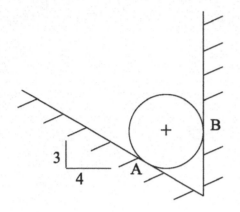

- ○ A. 96
- ○ B. 139
- ○ C. 150
- ○ D. 200

47.   A rod is shown in the figure below:

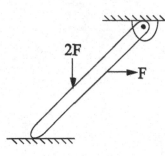

If the weight of the rod is neglected, which of the following is a correct free-body diagram?

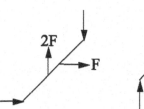 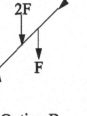 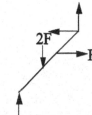 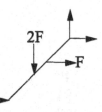

Option A   Option B   Option C   Option D

○ A.   Option A
○ B.   Option B
○ C.   Option C
○ D.   Option D

48.   Three forces act as shown below. The magnitude (N) of the resultant of the three forces is most nearly:

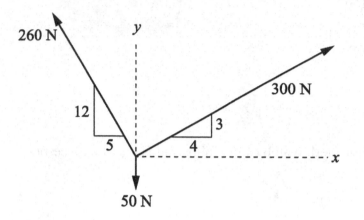

- ○ A.   140
- ○ B.   191
- ○ C.   370
- ○ D.   396

49. The moment of force **F** (N·m) shown below with respect to Point P is most nearly:

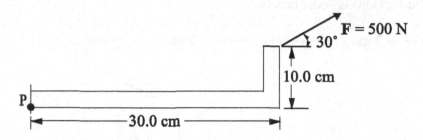

- ○ A.   31.7 ccw
- ○ B.   31.7 cw
- ○ C.   43.3 cw
- ○ D.   43.3 ccw

50. Beam AB has a distributed load as shown and supports at A and B. If the weight of the beam is negligible, the force R_B (kN) is most nearly:

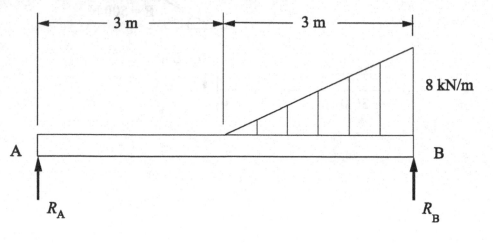

- ○ A. 24
- ○ B. 12
- ○ C. 10
- ○ D. 8

51.   In the figure below, the force (kips) in Member BC is most nearly:

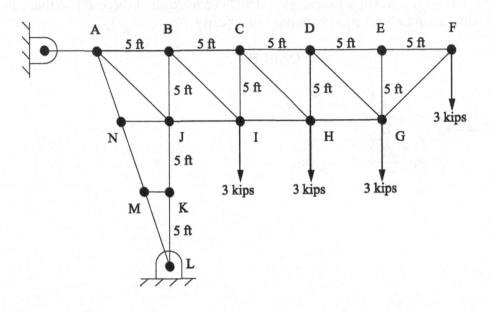

- A.   6
- B.   9
- C.   15
- D.   18

52. In the figure below, Block A weighs 50 N, Block B weighs 80 N, and Block C weighs 100 N. The coefficient of friction at all surfaces is 0.30. The maximum force **F** (N) that can be applied to Block B without disturbing equilibrium is most nearly:

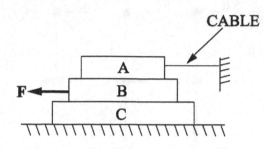

CABLE

- O A.   15
- O B.   54
- O C.   69
- O D.   84

53. The piston and cylinder of an internal combustion engine are shown in the following figure. If $\omega = 377$ rad/s, the piston speed (mm/s) when $\theta = 90°$ is most nearly:

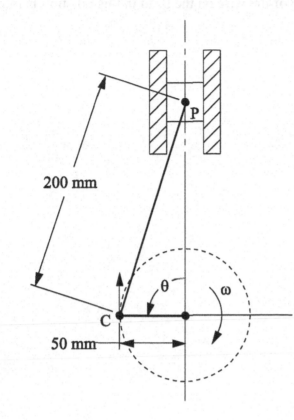

- ○ A.   0
- ○ B.   10,500
- ○ C.   18,850
- ○ D.   24,300

54.   A bead with a mass of 0.100 kg slides down a wire without friction along a circular path in a vertical plane as shown below. The speed of the bead along the wire in the position shown is 5.00 m/s. The magnitude of the force (N) of the wire on the bead in this position is most nearly:

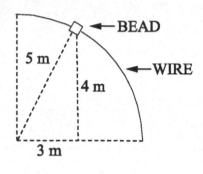

- ○ A.   0.285
- ○ B.   0.500
- ○ C.   0.785
- ○ D.   1.28

55. A particle traveled in a straight line in such a way that its distance s from a given point on that line after time t was $s = 20t^3 - t^4$. The rate of change of acceleration at time $t = 2$ is:

- A. 72
- B. 144
- C. 192
- D. 208

56. A bullet is fired with a horizontal velocity of 500 m/sec. It passes through a 3-kg block of wood, A, and becomes embedded in a second, 2.5-kg block of wood, B. The bullet causes Blocks A and B to start moving to the right with velocities of 3 m/sec and 5 m/sec, respectively. The mass G. of the bullet is most nearly:

- A. 43.4
- B. 45
- C. 45.2
- D. 477

57. A 2-kg block slides along a rough horizontal surface and slows to 10 m/s after traveling 20 m. If the kinetic coefficient of friction between the block and surface is 0.2, the initial speed (m/s) of the block was most nearly:

    ○ A.   10.0
    ○ B.   10.4
    ○ C.   13.4
    ○ D.   20.0

58. An object with a mass m of 1.50 kg moves without friction in a circular path as shown below. Attached to the object is a spring with a spring constant k of 400 N/m. The spring is undeformed when the object is at Point P, and the speed of the object at Point Q is 2.00 m/s.

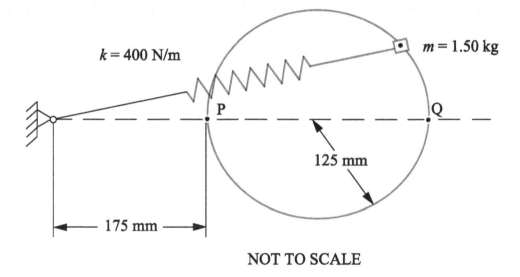

NOT TO SCALE

The translational kinetic energy (J) of the object at Point Q is most nearly:

    ○ A.   1.50
    ○ B.   3.00
    ○ C.   6.00
    ○ D.   29.40

59.   Which of the following is true when a circular shaft is subjected to torsion only?

    ○ A.   Maximum shear stress occurs at the outermost fibers.
    ○ B.   Maximum shear stress occurs at the center of the shaft.
    ○ C.   Constant shear stress occurs throughout the shaft.
    ○ D.   No shear stress is present throughout the shaft.

60.   The pressure gage in an air cylinder reads 1,680 kPa. The cylinder is constructed of a 12-mm rolled-steel plate with an internal diameter of 700 mm. The tangential stress (MPa) inside the tank is most nearly:

    ○ A.   25
    ○ B.   50
    ○ C.   77
    ○ D.   100

61. A test on a specimen results in major and minor principle stresses, as shown on the diagram below. One desires to know the stress state on a plane that is rotated +45° from the principal stress orientation.

Mark the point on the graph indicating the normal stress on the 45° plane.

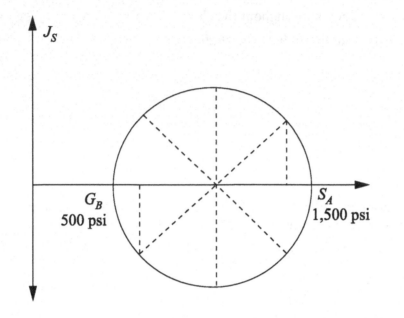

62.   The maximum inplane shear stress (ksi) in the element shown below is most nearly:

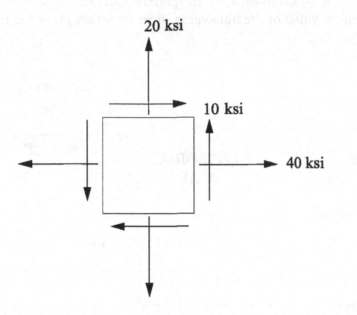

- ○ A.   10
- ○ B.   14.1
- ○ C.   44.1
- ○ D.   316

63. The T-shaped section shown below, made by welding two plates together, acts as a simply supported beam to carry a load of 10 kN/m on a 5.0-m span. Neglect the weight of the beam. For the loading shown, the maximum value of the transverse shear flow (kN/m) at the junction of the web and flange is most nearly:

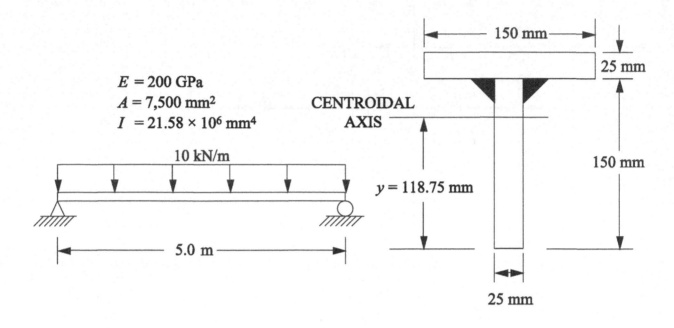

$E = 200$ GPa
$A = 7{,}500$ mm²
$I = 21.58 \times 10^6$ mm⁴

CENTROIDAL AXIS

10 kN/m

$y = 118.75$ mm

5.0 m

150 mm

25 mm

150 mm

25 mm

- O A.   95
- O B.   190
- O C.   204
- O D.   380

64. The shear diagram for a particular beam is shown below. All lines in the diagram are straight. The bending moment at each end of the beam is zero, and there are no concentrated couples along the beam. The maximum magnitude of the bending moment (kN·m) in the beam is most nearly:

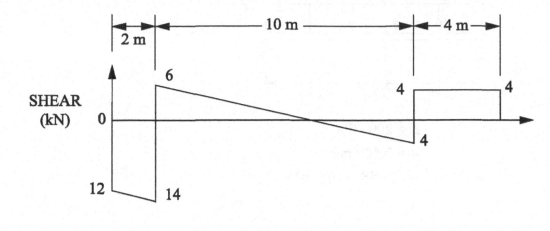

- ○ A.   8
- ○ B.   16
- ○ C.   18
- ○ D.   26

65. A simply supported beam carries a load of 10 kN/m on a 5.0-m span. If the weight of the beam is neglected, the maximum deflection (mm) of the beam is most nearly:

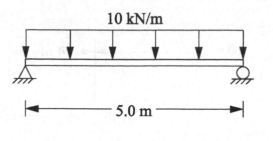

$$E = 200 \text{ GPa}$$
$$A = 7,500 \text{ mm}^2$$
$$I = 21.58 \times 10^{-6} \text{ m}^4$$

- ○ A. 10
- ○ B. 12
- ○ C. 15
- ○ D. 19

66. When a circular rod of unknown material is tested in tension, the original axial gage length of 100 mm increases by 0.2 mm. The diameter, originally 20 mm, decreases by 0.012 mm. The Poisson ratio for this material is most nearly:

- ○ A. −0.3
- ○ B. −0.06
- ○ C. 0.06
- ○ D. 0.3

67. A silver/copper binary phase diagram is shown below. An alloy that is 70% copper by weight is fully melted and allowed to cool slowly. The temperature at which solidification begins is most nearly:

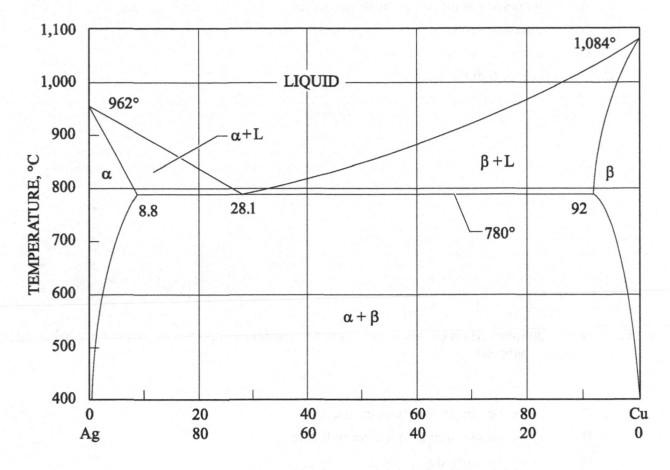

COMPOSITION, % BY WEIGHT

○ A.   962°C

○ B.   920°C

○ C.   800°C

○ D.   780°C

68.   When metal is cold-worked, all of the following generally occur **except:**

    ○ A.   recrystallization temperature decreases
    ○ B.   ductility decreases
    ○ C.   grains become equiaxed
    ○ D.   slip or twining takes place

69.   If an aluminum crimp connector were used to connect a copper wire to a battery, what would you expect to happen?

    ○ A.   Only the copper wire will corrode.
    ○ B.   Only the aluminum connector will corrode.
    ○ C.   Both will corrode.
    ○ D.   Nothing

70. A composite is fabricated from 60% by volume long, continuous glass fibers bonded within a polymer matrix. The elastic moduli of glass and polymer are 70 GPa and 5 GPa, respectively. The percentage of the tensile load applied along the direction of the fibers that is borne by the fibers is most nearly:

   ○ A.   42%
   ○ B.   60%
   ○ C.   93%
   ○ D.   95%

71. Glass is said to be an amorphous material. This means that it:

   ○ A.   has a high melting point
   ○ B.   is a supercooled vapor
   ○ C.   has large cubic crystals
   ○ D.   has no apparent crystal structure

72.   For the stress-strain curve below, mark the yield strength of the most ductile material.

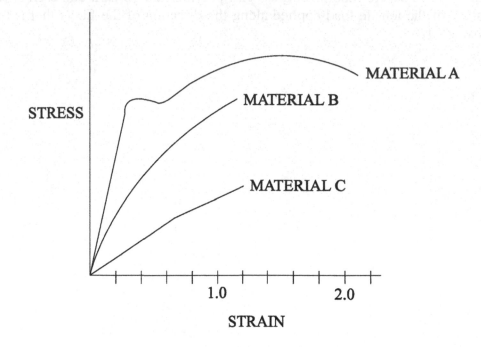

73.   A flat plate moving at a speed of 0.15 m/s is separated from a fixed plane surface by an oil film 0.25 mm thick. If the viscosity of the oil is 40×10^{-3} N·s/m², the shear stress in the oil film is most nearly:

  ○ A. 0.024 Pa
  ○ B. 2.4 Pa
  ○ C. 24 Pa
  ○ D. 2.4 kPa

74. Which of the following statements best describes conditions in turbulent flow?

- ○ A. Fluid particles move along a smooth, straight path.
- ○ B. Energy loss varies directly with the velocity.
- ○ C. Energy loss varies directly with the square of the velocity.
- ○ D. Reynolds number is always less than 2,000.

75. The rectangular homogeneous gate shown below is 3.00 m high × 1.00 m wide and has a frictionless hinge at the bottom. If the fluid on the left side of the gate has a density of 1,600 kg/m³, the magnitude of the force **F** (kN) required to keep the gate closed is most nearly:

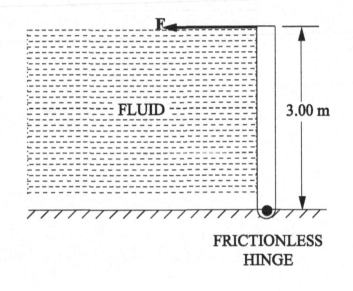

FRICTIONLESS
HINGE

- ○ A. 0
- ○ B. 22
- ○ C. 24
- ○ D. 220

76. A jet of water is shot vertically upward and hits a flat circular plate of mass M, as shown in the figure below. The diameter of the exhaust is 6 cm. If friction losses are neglected, the flow rate (m^3/s) of the water exiting the jet is most nearly:

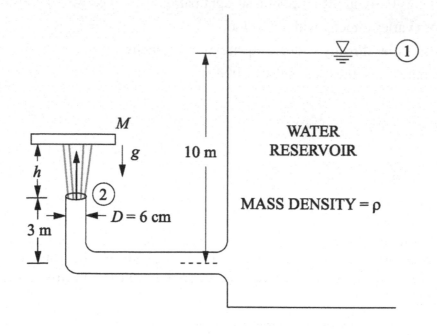

- ○ A. 0.015
- ○ B. 0.022
- ○ C. 0.033
- ○ D. 0.040

77.   A Newtonian fluid flows through 2-in. commercial steel pipe (I.D. = 0.0525 m).

      Liquid Properties:
            Density = 1.00 g/mL
            Viscosity = 1.05 cP
            Flow = 0.500 m^3/min

      The Reynolds number is most nearly:

- A. 1.93×10^3
- B. 7.94×10^3
- C. 1.93×10^5
- D. 1.15×10^7

78. The figure below represents a water-flow system in which water is pumped from the lake to the storage tank and also flows from the lake through the turbine. Darcy friction factors are given for the pipe flows:

$$f = h_f \frac{D}{L}\frac{2g}{V^2} \quad \text{(Fanning friction factors are one-fourth as large.)}$$

Specific weight of water = 9,800 N/m^3
Atmospheric pressure = 1.01×10^5 N/m^2

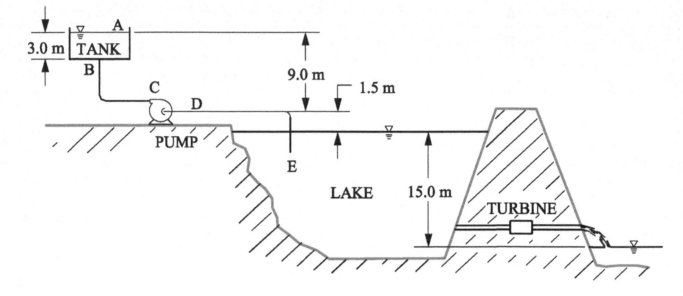

NOT TO SCALE

With Tank A and Pipe BC filled with water to the level shown, but with no flow, the gage pressure (kPa) at Point C is most nearly:

- ○ A. 9
- ○ B. 29
- ○ C. 88
- ○ D. 190

79. The level in a retention basin is normally controlled with a pipe as shown in the figure below. The pipe has an I.D. of 30 cm. The equivalent length of the pipe (including the elbows, entrance effect, and discharge) is 6.0 m. Relative roughness is 0.0005. The fluid has the following properties:

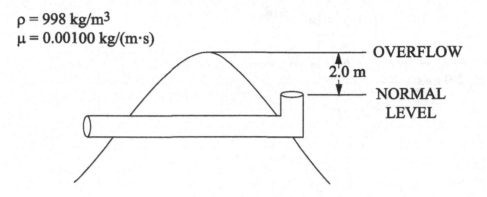

$\rho = 998 \text{ kg/m}^3$
$\mu = 0.00100 \text{ kg/(m·s)}$

Assuming a Reynolds number of 200,000, the Moody friction factor f is most nearly:

- ○ A.   0.017
- ○ B.   0.019
- ○ C.   0.022
- ○ D.   0.032

80.   The pitot tube shown below is placed at a point where the velocity is 2.0 m/s. The specific gravity of the fluid is 2.0, and the upper portion of the manometer contains air. The reading h (m) on the manometer is most nearly:

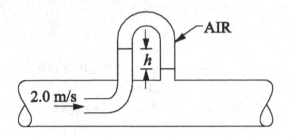

- A.   20.0
- B.   10.0
- C.   0.40
- D.   0.20

81. A 30-L cylinder is filled with air to a pressure of 10 MPa. The valve to the cylinder is then closed. Thermodynamic data for dry air are given in the table below.

Pressure (MPa)	Property	Temperature (K)						
		280	300	350	400	450	500	600
4	v	0.0198	0.0214	0.0252	0.0290	0.0327	0.0364	0.0438
	u	191.0	206.1	243.8	281.0	318.4	355.9	431.7
	h	270.2	291.7	344.6	397.0	449.2	501.5	606.9
6	v	0.0131	0.0142	0.0169	0.0194	0.0220	0.0245	0.0294
	u	184.5	200.4	239.0	277.6	315.1	353.6	430.4
	h	263.1	285.6	340.4	394.0	447.1	500.6	606.8
8	v	0.0098	0.0107	0.0127	0.0147	0.0166	0.0185	0.0223
	u	182.3	198.1	237.4	275.5	313.7	351.8	428.3
	h	260.8	283.7	339.0	393.1	446.5	499.8	606.7
10	v	0.0078	0.0086	0.0102	0.0118	0.0134	0.0149	0.0180
	u	177.9	194.4	234.5	273.3	311.3	350.0	426.6
	h	256.4	279.9	336.5	391.3	445.3	499.0	606.0

v = specific volume, m³/kg; u = internal energy, kJ/kg; h = enthalpy, kJ/kg

Assume the temperature in the cylinder immediately after filling is 600 K and that no air has been removed from the cylinder. The pressure (MPa) in the cylinder a week after filling (when the temperature is 300 K) is most nearly:

- A. 4.17
- B. 4.94
- C. 5.06
- D. 5.20

82. The work (kJ) required to compress 1,000 L of an ideal gas to 500 L at a constant pressure of 100 kPa in a closed system is most nearly:

- A. 0.2
- B. 5
- C. 50
- D. 600

83. Air flows through a horizontal duct having a cross-sectional area of 0.5 m^2 at a particular location along the length of the duct. The air properties are:

$C_p = 1,000 \text{ J/(kg·K)}$
$R = 287 \text{ J/(kg·K)}$
$k = 1.4$

The air is slowed down reversibly and adiabatically from 150 m/s and 300 K to 50 m/s as the duct area increases. The air temperature at the point where the velocity is 50 m/s is most nearly:

- A. 239 K
- B. 300 K
- C. 310 K
- D. 320 K

84. The following data were obtained from a test on a centrifugal fan:

> Fluid = Air at 300 K, 101 kPa
> Fan wheel diameter = 0.5 m
> Speed = 1,000 rpm
> Flow rate = 3.0 m³/s
> Pressure rise = 0.90 kPa
> Power = 4.0 kW

The efficiency of the fan at the test conditions is most nearly:

- ○ A.　　0.38
- ○ B.　　0.53
- ○ C.　　0.68
- ○ D.　　0.82

85. The photoelectric effect refers to a process in which:

- ○ A.　　an electron is converted into two photons
- ○ B.　　electrons release light from a metal target
- ○ C.　　light releases electrons from a metal target
- ○ D.　　a quantum of energy is converted into a photon

86. The switch on the circuit below has been in Position 1 for a long time before $t = 0$, at which time it is moved to Position 2. The time constant (s) for the circuit just before the switching is:

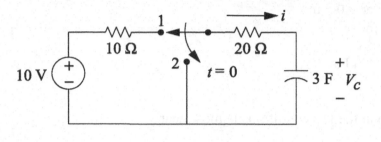

- O A. 90
- O B. 60
- O C. 30
- O D. 3

87. The connecting wires and the battery in the circuit shown below have negligible resistance. The current (amperes) through the 6-Ω resistor is most nearly:

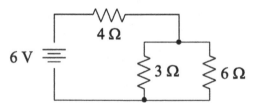

- O A. 1/3
- O B. 1/2
- O C. 1
- O D. 3/2

88.   The Thevenin equivalent voltage (V) at Terminals ab in the circuit shown below is most nearly:

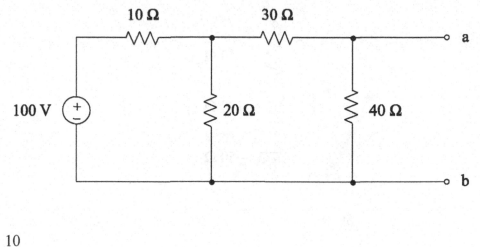

    ○ A.   10
    ○ B.   35
    ○ C.   61
    ○ D.   100

89. Series-connected circuit elements are shown in the figure below. Which of the following impedance diagrams is correct according to conventional notation?

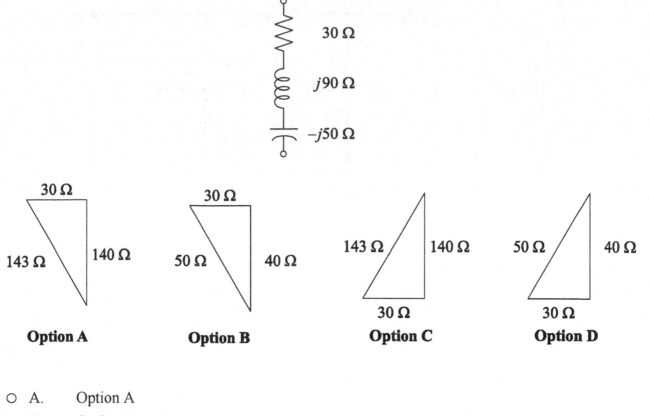

- ○ A. Option A
- ○ B. Option B
- ○ C. Option C
- ○ D. Option D

90.   If the complex power is 1,500 VA with a power factor of 0.866 lagging, the reactive power (VAR) is most nearly:

- ○ A.   0
- ○ B.   750
- ○ C.   1,300
- ○ D.   1,500

91. The figure below shows a Rankine cycle with water as the working medium. Data are given directly on the figure. Disregard pressure losses in the piping, steam boiler, and superheater, and neglect kinetic and potential energy effects. Assume that there is a steady flow with adiabatic expansion in the turbine. Use steam tables as needed for fluid properties.

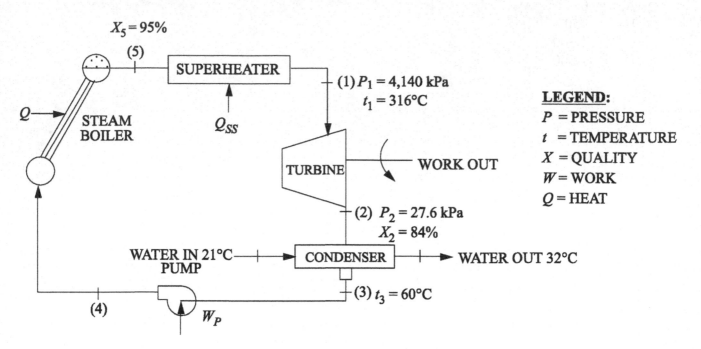

If it is assumed the fluid is incompressible, the pump work (kJ/kg) is most nearly:

- ○ A.   0.0291
- ○ B.   2.40
- ○ C.   2.88
- ○ D.   4.19

92. Which of the following statements about flow through an insulated valve is most accurate?

- ○ A.   The enthalpy rises.
- ○ B.   Pressure increases sharply.
- ○ C.   Temperature increases sharply.
- ○ D.   The upstream and downstream enthalpies are equal.

93.   A heat engine operates in a closed system on the cycle shown, which is a series of three reversible processes. The process from State 1 to State 2 is a constant-pressure process at 3,500 kPa. The process from State 2 to State 3 is a constant-volume process at 1 m³. The process from State 3 to State 1 is a constant-temperature process at 2°C. The volume at State 1 is half the volume of State 3. Air is the working fluid, which may be assumed to behave as an ideal gas under process conditions.

Consider air to be an ideal gas with the following properties:

$C_p = 1.00$ kJ/(kg·K)
$C_v = 0.718$ kJ/(kg·K)
$k = 1.40$
$R = 0.287$ kJ/(kg·K)

The heat (kJ) transferred during the process from State 2 to State 3 is most nearly:

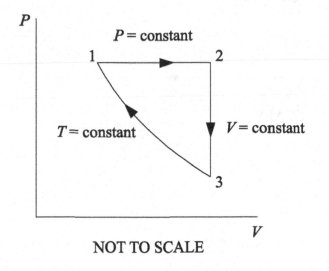

NOT TO SCALE

- ○ A.   –3,700
- ○ B.   –4,400
- ○ C.   –6,100
- ○ D.   –7,200

94.   Refer to the Carnot power cycle shown. The working medium is 1 kg of air as an ideal gas. The cycle has a thermal efficiency of 48%. The heat transfer to air during the isothermal expansion is 60 kJ. At the beginning of the isothermal expansion, the pressure is 9 bars and the volume is 0.3 m^3. The volume (m^3) at the end of the isothermal expansion process is most nearly:

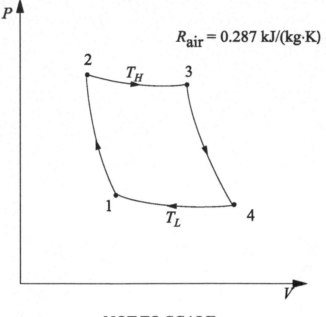

$$R_{air} = 0.287 \text{ kJ/(kg·K)}$$

NOT TO SCALE

○ A.   0.375
○ B.   0.451
○ C.   0.521
○ D.   0.623

95.   Hot air at 200°C flows across a 50°C surface. If the heat transfer coefficient is 72 W/(m²·°C), the heat transfer rate (W) over 2 m² of the surface is most nearly:

○ A.   300
○ B.   5,625
○ C.   11,250
○ D.   21,600

96.   An insulated tank contains half liquid and half vapor by volume in equilibrium. The release of a small quantity of the vapor without the addition of heat will cause:

○ A.   evaporation of some liquid in the tank
○ B.   superheating of the vapor in the tank
○ C.   a rise in temperature
○ D.   an increase in enthalpy

97. A gas at a temperature of 27°C occupies 5 L at 1 atm. $R = 0.082$ L·atm/(mol·K). If the pressure is increased to 2 atm and the temperature is increased to 100°C, the volume (L) of the gas will be most nearly:

    ○ A.   3.11
    ○ B.   5.00
    ○ C.   6.22
    ○ D.   9.26

98. An insulated container contains 15 kg of water, a heater, and a motorized stirrer. The heater is run for sufficient time to provide 2,000 J of energy to the water. The stirrer adds 4,000 J of energy to the water. The thermal masses of the heater and stirrer are negligible compared to the water. The temperature increase of the water is most nearly:

    ○ A.   0.064°C
    ○ B.   0.072°C
    ○ C.   0.096°C
    ○ D.   0.40°C

99.   In the iron-iron carbide phase diagram, where is the eutectoid point?

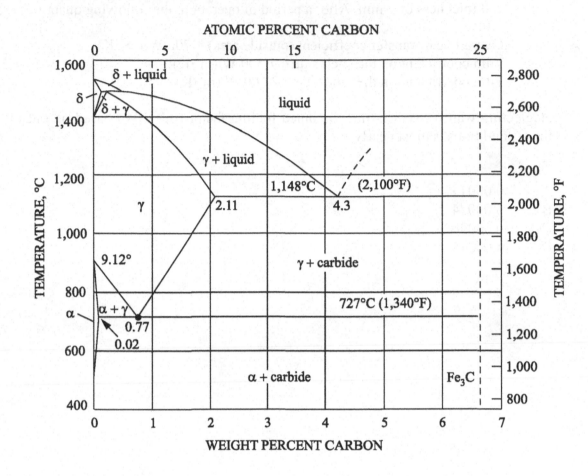

○ A.   727°C, 0.77% carbon

○ B.   1,148°C, 2.11% carbon

○ C.   1,148°C, 4.3% carbon

○ D.   2,700°C, 0.5% carbon

100. A multitube heat exchanger for cooling a process fluid with water contains 25-mm O.D. tubes with a wall thickness of 3 mm. After a period of operation, the following quantities are known:

Overall heat-transfer coefficient (outside area) = 700 W/(m$^2 \cdot$K)
Film coefficient on the shell side = 1,500 W/(m$^2 \cdot$K)
Film coefficient on the tube side = 2,500 W/(m$^2 \cdot$K)

Neglecting wall resistance, the combined fouling factor (m$^2 \cdot$K/W) based on outside area under these conditions is most nearly:

- A.   0.00015
- B.   0.00024
- C.   0.00036
- D.   0.00046

FE OTHER DISCIPLINES SOLUTIONS

Detailed solutions for each question begin on the next page.

1	A	26	B	51	D	76	C
2	A	27	C	52	B	77	C
3	D	28	C	53	C	78	C
4	A	29	C	54	A	79	B
5	D	30	A	55	A	80	D
6	B	31	A	56	A	81	B
7	B	32	A	57	C	82	C
8	C	33	A, C, D, E	58	B	83	C
9	D	34	D	59	A	84	C
10	D	35	C	60	B	85	C
11	C	36	D	61	see solution	86	A
12	A	37	C	62	B	87	A
13	D	38	C	63	B	88	B
14	A	39	D	64	D	89	D
15	D	40	D	65	D	90	B
16	B	41	B	66	D	91	D
17	B	42	A	67	B	92	D
18	A	43	B	68	C	93	B
19	C	44	D	69	B	94	A
20	50	45	A	70	D	95	D
21	D	46	C	71	D	96	A
22	A	47	C	72	see solution	97	A
23	C	48	D	73	C	98	C
24	B	49	A	74	C	99	A
25	see solution	50	C	75	C	100	B

FE OTHER DISCIPLINES SOLUTIONS

1. Refer to the Mathematics section of the *FE Reference Handbook*.

$(x - h)^2 + (y - k)^2 + (z - m)^2 = r^2$ with center at (h, k, m)

$(x - 0)^2 + (y - 1)^2 + (z - (-2))^2 = r^2$

$x^2 + (y - 1)^2 + (z + 2)^2 = 81$

THE CORRECT ANSWER IS: A

2.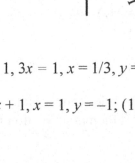

$y = -x$

$y = x$

$y = -2x + 1$

intersection of $y = x$ and $y = -x$ is $(0, 0)$

intersection of $y = x$ and $y = -2x + 1$ is $x = -2x + 1$, $3x = 1$, $x = 1/3$, $y = 1/3$; $(1/3, 1/3)$

intersection of $y = -x$ and $y = -2x + 1$ is $-x = -2x + 1$, $x = 1$, $y = -1$; $(1, -1)$

THE CORRECT ANSWER IS: A

3. $\int (x^3 - x + 1)\,dx = \dfrac{x^4}{4} - \dfrac{x^2}{2} + x + C$

THE CORRECT ANSWER IS: D

4. Define a differential strip with length $(x - 0)$ and height dy.

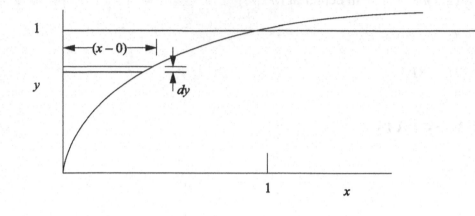

$$\int dA = \int_0^1 x\,dy = \int_0^1 y^{3/2}\,dy = \frac{y^{5/2}}{5/2}\bigg|_0^1 = \frac{2}{5}$$

THE CORRECT ANSWER IS: A

5. $\dfrac{d^2 y}{dt^2} + 6\dfrac{dy}{dt} + 25y = x(t)$

The characteristic equation is $D^2 + 6D + 25 = 0$

Referring to Second-Order Linear Homogeneous Differential Equations with Constant Coefficients in the Mathematics section of the *FE Reference Handbook*:

$a = 6$
$a^2 = 36$
$b = 25$
$4b = 100$

Since $a^2 = 36$ is less than $4b = 100$, the system is underdamped.

THE CORRECT ANSWER IS: D

6. The characteristic equation for a first-order linear homogeneous differential equation is:

$$r + 5 = 0$$

which has a root at $r = -5$.

Refer to Differential Equations in the Mathematics section of the *FE Reference Handbook*. The form of the solution is then:

$$y = Ce^{-\alpha t} \text{ where } \alpha = a \text{ and } \quad a = 5 \text{ for this problem}$$

C is determined from the boundary condition.

$$1 = Ce^{-5(0)}$$
$$C = 1$$

Then, $y = e^{-5t}$

THE CORRECT ANSWER IS: B

7.

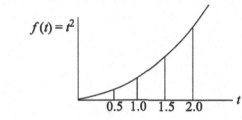

Refer to the Mathematics section of the *FE Reference Handbook*.

$$\text{Area} = \frac{0.5}{2}\left[0^2 + 2(0.5)^2 + 2(1.0)^2 + 2(1.5)^2 + (2)^2\right] = 2.75$$

THE CORRECT ANSWER IS: B

8. The roots of a function are defined as points where $F = 0$.

    In this case, divide the polynomials:

    $$
    \begin{array}{r}
    x^2 + 5x + 6 \\
    x+1\overline{\smash{\big)}\, x^3 + 6x^2 + 11x + 6} \\
    \underline{x^3 + x^2} \\
    5x^2 + 11x \\
    \underline{5x^2 + 5x} \\
    6x + 6 \\
    \underline{6x + 6} \\
    0
    \end{array}
    $$

    $x^2 + 5x + 6$ factors to $(x + 2)(x + 3)$. Therefore, the roots of F are $x = -2$ and $x = -3$

    THE CORRECT ANSWER IS: C

9. $$\frac{(1-i)^2}{(1+i)^2} = \frac{1 - 2i + i^2}{1 + 2i + i^2} = \frac{1 - 1 - 2i}{1 - 1 + 2i} = \frac{-i}{i} = -1$$

    THE CORRECT ANSWER IS: D

10. Refer to Vectors in the Mathematics section of the *FE Reference Handbook*.

    $$\mathbf{a} \times \mathbf{b} = \left[(3)(2) - (4)(0)\right]\mathbf{i} + \left[(4)(3) - (2)(-2)\right]\mathbf{j} + \left[(-2)(0) - (3)(3)\right]\mathbf{k}$$
    $$= \left[6 - 0\right]\mathbf{i} + \left[12 + 4\right]\mathbf{j} + \left[0 - 9\right]\mathbf{k}$$
    $$= 6\mathbf{i} + 16\mathbf{j} - 9\mathbf{k}$$

    THE CORRECT ANSWER IS: D

11. The cross product of vectors **A** and **B** is a vector perpendicular to **A** and **B**.

$$\begin{vmatrix} \mathbf{i} & \mathbf{j} & \mathbf{k} \\ 2 & 4 & 0 \\ 1 & 1 & -1 \end{vmatrix} = \mathbf{i}(-4) - \mathbf{j}(-2-0) + \mathbf{k}(2-4) = -4\mathbf{i} + 2\mathbf{j} - 2\mathbf{k}$$

To obtain a unit vector, divide by the magnitude.

$$\text{Magnitude} = \sqrt{(-4)^2 + 2^2 + (-2)^2} = \sqrt{24} = 2\sqrt{6}$$

$$\frac{-4\mathbf{i} + 2\mathbf{j} - 2\mathbf{k}}{2\sqrt{6}} = \frac{-2\mathbf{i} + \mathbf{j} - \mathbf{k}}{\sqrt{6}}$$

THE CORRECT ANSWER IS: C

12.

$$\left(\vec{\mathbf{B}} \times \vec{\mathbf{C}}\right) = \begin{vmatrix} \vec{\mathbf{i}} & \vec{\mathbf{j}} & \vec{\mathbf{k}} \\ -1 & 2 & 2 \\ 2 & 3 & -4 \end{vmatrix}$$

$$= \mathbf{i}(-8-6) - \mathbf{j}(4-4) + \mathbf{k}(-3-4)$$

$$= -14\mathbf{i} - 7\mathbf{k}$$

$$\left(\vec{\mathbf{B}} \times \vec{\mathbf{C}}\right) \cdot \mathbf{A} = \left(-14\mathbf{i} + 0\mathbf{j} - 7\mathbf{k}\right) \cdot \left(5\mathbf{i} - 3\mathbf{j} + 6\mathbf{k}\right)$$

$$= (-14)(5) + (-7)(6)$$

$$= -70 - 42 = -112$$

THE CORRECT ANSWER IS: A

13. From Dispersion, Mean, Median, and Mode Values in the Engineering Probability and Statistics section of the *FE Reference Handbook*:

$$\sigma = \sqrt{\frac{1}{N}\sum(x_1 - \mu)^2}$$

$$\sigma = \sqrt{\frac{4(11-12)^2 + 1(12-12)^2 + 2(13-12)^2 + 1(14-12)^2}{8}} = \sqrt{\frac{10}{8}}$$

$$\sigma = 1.118$$

THE CORRECT ANSWER IS: D

14. Find the probability that the population mean (μ) is less than 150 psi if a sample mean $\overline{X}$ is 153 psi and the population standard deviation (σ) is 3 psi:

$$\mu = \overline{X} \pm Z_{\alpha/2}\frac{\sigma}{\sqrt{n}}$$

$$150 = 153 \pm Z_{\alpha/2}\frac{3}{\sqrt{8}}$$

$$Z_{\alpha/2} = \frac{(153-150)\sqrt{8}}{3} = \sqrt{8}$$

$$Z_{\alpha/2} = 2.83$$

Refer to the Table of Unit Normal Distribution in the Engineering Probability and Statistics section of the *FE Reference Handbook*.

$$X = Z_{\alpha/2} = 2.83$$
$$P(X \le 2.83) = R(2.83) \approx 0.0026$$

THE CORRECT ANSWER IS: A

FE OTHER DISCIPLINES SOLUTIONS

15. Refer to the Engineering Probability and Statistics section of the *FE Reference Handbook*.

There is only one throw, 6 and 6, that sums to 12. There are 36 possible rolls of the dice and therefore 35/36 will have a sum less than 12.

$35/36 = 0.972$

THE CORRECT ANSWER IS: D

16. Refer to the Engineering Probability and Statistics section of the *FE Reference Handbook*.

Binomial distribution
$p = 0.5$ (chance of getting a head)
$q = 0.5$ (chance of not getting a head)
$n = 10$ (number of trials)
$x = 4$ (number of heads)

$$P_{10}(4) = \frac{10!}{4!6!}(0.5^4)(0.5^6) = \frac{(10)(9)(8)(7)}{(4)(3)(2)(1)}(0.5)^{10}$$

$$= 0.2051$$

THE CORRECT ANSWER IS: B

17. Accuracy increases with increasing sample size.

THE CORRECT ANSWER IS: B

18. Use equations from the Engineering Probability and Statistics section of the *FE Reference Handbook* with data from the following table.

x	y	xy	x^2
2.3	5.6	12.88	5.29
1.2	4.1	4.92	1.44
4.2	8.6	36.12	17.64
6.3	10.1	63.63	36.69
$\sum =$ 14.0	28.4	117.55	64.06

$$S_{xy} = \sum x_i y_i - \left(\frac{1}{n}\right)\left(\sum x_i\right)\left(\sum y_i\right) = 117.55 - \left(\frac{1}{4}\right)(14)(28.4)$$
$$= 18.15$$

$$S_{xx} = \sum x_i^2 - \left(\frac{1}{n}\right)\left(\sum x_i\right)^2 = 64.06 - \left(\frac{1}{4}\right)(14)^2$$
$$= 15.06$$

$b = S_{xy}/S_{xx} = 18.15/15.06 = 1.2052$

$\bar{x} = 14/4 = 3.5$ and $\bar{y} = 28.4/4 = 7.1$

$a = \bar{y} - b\bar{x} = 7.1 - 1.2052(3.5) = 2.8818$

$y = 2.88 + 1.20x$

THE CORRECT ANSWER IS: A

19. Refer to the atomic weights in the Periodic Table in the Chemistry section of the *FE Reference Handbook*.

$H_2SO_4 \rightarrow$ $H_2 = 2(1) = 2$
$S = 1(32) = 32$
$O_4 = 4(16) = 64$
$\underline{}$
98

THE CORRECT ANSWER IS: C

20. The atomic number of an element corresponds to the number of protons in the atom. According to the period table, the atomic number of tin (Sn) is 50.

THE CORRECT ANSWER IS: 50

21. $Pv = nRT$

$R = 0.08206$ L·atm/mol·K

$(1)(v) = (1)(0.08206)(546)$

$v = 44.8$ L

THE CORRECT ANSWER IS: D

22. Oxidation reduction reactions require an exchange of electrons. By inspection, the valence states of answers B, C, and D do change. There is no change of valence state in $CaCO_3 \rightarrow CaO + CO_2$.

$Ca^{+2}C^{+4}O_3{}^{-2} \rightarrow Ca^{+2}O^{-2} + C^{+4}O_2{}^{-4}$

$C^{+4}O_2{}^{-4} + C^0 \rightarrow 2C^{+2}O^{-2}$

$Fe + S^2 \rightarrow Fe^{+2}S^{-2}$

$2S^{+4}O_2{}^{-4} + O_2 \rightarrow 2S^{+6}O_3{}^{-6}$

THE CORRECT ANSWER IS: A

23. One gram formula weight of NaOH is 40 g; therefore, 4 g/L of NaOH will form 1 L of 0.1 normal NaOH solution. One liter of 0.1 normal HCl solution is required to neutralize the NaOH.

THE CORRECT ANSWER IS: C

24.   Refer to the Chemistry section of the *FE Reference Handbook* for the equilibrium constant of a chemical reaction.

$$4A + B \leftrightarrow 2C + 2D$$

THE CORRECT ANSWER IS: B

25.   Refer to the Chemistry section of the *FE Reference Handbook*.

In a balanced reaction, the number of atoms of each element must be the same on both sides of the reaction.

Carbon: $A*1 + B*0 = C*1 + D*0$ $A = C$
Hydrogen: $A*4 + B*0 = C*0 + D*2$ $2A = D$
Oxygen: $A*0 + B*2 = C*2 + D*1$ $2B = 2C + D$

Let $A = 1$, then $C = 1$
                        $D = 2$
                        $B = 2$

$$CH_4 + 2O_2 \rightarrow CO_2 + 2H_2O$$

__1__ CH_4 __2__ $O_2 \rightarrow$ __1__ $CO_2 +$ __2__ H_2O

THE CORRECT ANSWER IS SHOWN ABOVE.

26.   Refer to the Thermodynamics section of the *FE Reference Handbook*. Use the ideal gas formula:

$$PV = mRT$$

$$P = \frac{mRT}{V}$$

$$R = \frac{8,314 \text{ J}}{\text{kmole} \cdot \text{K}} \frac{\text{kmol}}{28 \text{ kg}} = 297 \frac{\text{J}}{\text{kg} \cdot \text{K}}$$

$$P = \frac{(100 \text{ kg})\left(297 \frac{\text{J}}{\text{kg} \cdot \text{K}}\right)(343 \text{ K})}{100 \text{ m}^3}$$

$$= 102,000 \frac{\text{J}}{\text{m}^3}$$

$$= 102,000 \frac{\text{N} \cdot \text{m}}{\text{m}^3}$$

$$= 102,000 \frac{\text{N}}{\text{m}^2}$$

$$= 102 \text{ kPa}$$

THE CORRECT ANSWER IS: B

27. $R = R_o \left[1 + \alpha(T - T_o)\right]$

$$\Delta R = \frac{dR}{dT} \Delta T$$

$$= R_o \alpha \Delta T$$

$$= (100 \; \Omega)(0.004°\text{C}^{-1})(10°\text{C})$$

$$= 4.0 \; \Omega$$

THE CORRECT ANSWER IS: C

28. The area under the flow vs. time from time = 0 until time = 24 hours results in the volume passing the measuring point.

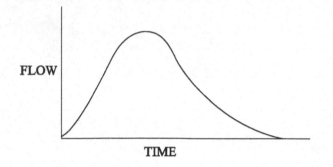

FLOW

TIME

THE CORRECT ANSWER IS: C

29. The frequency of the continuous signal is $f_n = \dfrac{1}{t_{n+2} - t_n} = \dfrac{1}{2\Delta t} = \dfrac{1}{2} s^{-1}$

Minimum sampling frequency f_s is $f_s = 2f_n = 1\,s^{-1}$ or 1 sample/sec

THE CORRECT ANSWER IS: C

30. K = 2 gives A = 17/2 = 8.5
K = 3 gives A = 8.5/3 = 2.83
K = 4 gives A = 2.83/4 = 0.71

THE CORRECT ANSWER IS: A

31. Refer to Section C of the *Model Rules* in the Ethics section of the *FE Reference Handbook.*

THE CORRECT ANSWER IS: A

32. Refer to the NCEES Rules of Professional Conduct in the Ethics section of the *FE Reference Handbook.* Licensees may take assignments only when qualified by education or experience in the specific technical fields of engineering involved.

THE CORRECT ANSWER IS: A

FE OTHER DISCIPLINES SOLUTIONS

33. The *FE Reference Handbook* contains information from the NCEES *Model Rules*, particularly the sections that identify a licensee's obligation to the public, employers and clients, and other licensees. Thus, other licensees, the public, employers, and clients are correct options. The licensee's alma mater and the court system are not correct.

THE CORRECT ANSWERS ARE: A, C, D, AND E

34. Refer to the Ethics section of the *FE Reference Handbook*. Section A in the Rules of Professional Conduct dictates the reporting of violations.

THE CORRECT ANSWER IS: D

35. Nicotine has the lowest LD_{50} of the group (1 mg/kg).

THE CORRECT ANSWER IS: C

36. Steel-toed boots would not protect someone from basic, common dangers in a chemistry lab.

THE CORRECT ANSWER IS: D

37. Volume of contaminated air $= \left(\dfrac{10^6 \, m^3 \, air}{1 \, m^3 \, benzene}\right)\left(\dfrac{m^3}{mol} benzene\right)\left(\dfrac{100 \, g \, benzene}{78 \, g/mol}\right)$

$\dfrac{m^3 \, benzene}{mol} = \dfrac{RT}{P} = 8.314 \times 10^{-3} \dfrac{kPa \cdot m^3}{mol \cdot K} \cdot (298 \, K)/(101 \, kPa)$

$= 2.45 \times 10^{-2} \, m^3/mol$

Volume of contaminated air $= 10^6 \dfrac{m^3 \, air}{m^3 \, benzene} \left(2.45 \times 10^{-2} \dfrac{m^3 \, benzene}{mol}\right)(1.282 \, mol \, benzene)$

$= 3.14 \times 10^4 \, m^3$

THE CORRECT ANSWER IS: C

38. Ground fault interrupters are required for exterior residential power outlets.

THE CORRECT ANSWER IS: C

39.

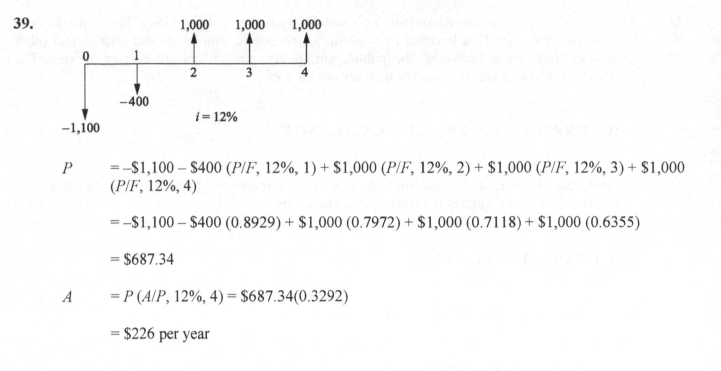

P = –\$1,100 – \$400 (P/F, 12%, 1) + \$1,000 (P/F, 12%, 2) + \$1,000 (P/F, 12%, 3) + \$1,000 (P/F, 12%, 4)

= –\$1,100 – \$400 (0.8929) + \$1,000 (0.7972) + \$1,000 (0.7118) + \$1,000 (0.6355)

= \$687.34

A = P (A/P, 12%, 4) = \$687.34(0.3292)

= \$226 per year

THE CORRECT ANSWER IS: D

40. Refer to the Engineering Economics section of the *FE Reference Handbook.*

PW = –3,600 – 400 (P/A, 10%, 7) + 600 (P/F, 10%, 7)

= –3,600 – 400 (4.8684) + 600 (0.5132)

= –5,239.4

THE CORRECT ANSWER IS: D

41. Refer to the definition of break-even analysis in the Engineering Economics section of the *FE Reference Handbook.*

THE CORRECT ANSWER IS: B

42. The annual unit costs for the hand tool method and the automated method are:

$1.50 (5,000) = $7,500
$0.50 (5,000) = $2,500

Thus the annual savings is:

$7,500 − $2,500 = $5,000, which is a benefit of the automated method.

This benefit requires an additional investment of:

$15,000 − $1,000 = $14,000

Therefore the payback is:

$14,000/$5,000 = 2.8 yr

THE CORRECT ANSWER IS: A

43. First-year depreciation cost $= \dfrac{\$200,000 - \$10,000}{10 \text{ years}} = \$19,000/\text{year}.$

Total costs = Fixed annual + depreciation + (variable/unit) × (N units)
1st year   = 150,000 + 19,000 + (0.30 + 0.65 + 0.20) × (N)

Revenue = 2.00 N
Profit = 2.00 N − 169,000 − 1.15 N
E (profit) = 0.85 E (N) − 169,000
E (N) = 0.1 (500,000) + 0.2 (600,000) + 0.4 (700,000) + 0.2 (800,000) + 0.1 (900,000)
        = 700,000
E (profit) = 0.85 (700,000) − 169,000 = $426,000/year

THE CORRECT ANSWER IS: B

44. The easiest way to solve this problem is to look at the present worth of each option.

The present worth values are all given by

$$P = \text{First Cost} + \text{Annual Cost} \times (P/A, 12\%, 8) - \text{Salvage Value} \times (P/F, 12\%, 8)$$
$$= \text{First Cost} + \text{Annual Cost} \times 4.9676 - \text{Salvage Value} \times 0.4039$$

$P(A) = \$25,000 + \$8,000(4.9676) - \$2,500(0.4039)$
$P(B) = \$35,000 + \$6,000(4.9676) - \$3,500(0.4039)$
$P(C) = \$20,000 + \$9,000(4.9676) - \$2,000(0.4039)$
$P(D) = \$40,000 + \$5,000(4.9676) - \$4,000(0.4039)$

Then
$P(A) = \$63,731$
$P(B) = \$63,392$
$P(C) = \$63,901$
$P(D) = \$63,222$

The cash flows are all costs, so the two most preferable projects, those with the lowest present worth costs, are B and D, and the difference between them is $170.

THE CORRECT ANSWER IS: D

45. Refer to Resolution of a Force in the Statics section of the *FE Reference Handbook.*

$$R_x = \sum F_{xi}, \qquad R_y = \sum F_{yi}, \qquad i = 1, 2, 3$$

$$R_x = 2.12 + 5 \cos 105° = 2.12 - 1.29 = 0.83 \text{ N}$$

$$R_y = 2.12 + 5 \sin 105° = 2.12 + 4.83 = 6.95 \text{ N}$$

$$R = \sqrt{R_x^2 + R_y^2} = \sqrt{0.83^2 + 6.95^2} = 6.999 \text{ N}$$

THE CORRECT ANSWER IS: A

46. $\Sigma F_y = 0 = -120 + \dfrac{4}{5} A$

$A = 150 \text{ N}$

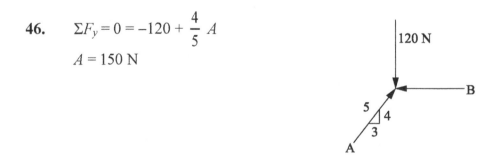

THE CORRECT ANSWER IS: C

FE OTHER DISCIPLINES SOLUTIONS

47. The upper pin connection has two force reactions. The lower surface supports the member with a normal force.

THE CORRECT ANSWER IS: C

48. $R_y = \Sigma F_y = \dfrac{12}{13}(260) + \dfrac{3}{5}(300) - 50 = 370$

$R_x = \Sigma F_x = -\dfrac{5}{13}(260) + \dfrac{4}{5}(300) = 140$

$R = \sqrt{R_x^2 + R_y^2} = \sqrt{370^2 + 140^2}$

$R = 396$ N

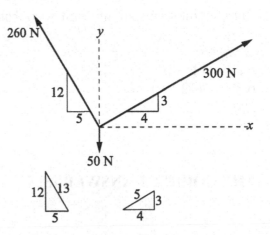

THE CORRECT ANSWER IS: D

49. $F_H = 500 \cos 30° = 433$

$F_V = 500 \sin 30° = 250$

$M_P = 250(0.30) - 433(0.10) = 31.7$ N·m ccw

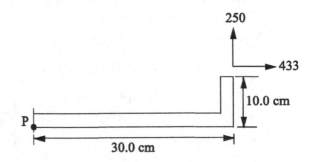

THE CORRECT ANSWER IS: A

50. Refer to Systems of Forces in the Statics section of the *FE Reference Handbook*.

The triangular force distribution can be replaced with a concentrated force **F** acting through the centroid of the triangle. The magnitude of **F** is numerically equal to the area of the triangle.

F = 1/2 (base)(height) = 1/2 (3 m)(8 kN/m)
F = 12 kN

Sum the moments about Point A so that the only unknown is R_B.

$\Sigma M_A = 0$
$6 R_B - 5 \mathbf{F} = 0$
$6 R_B - 5(12 \text{ kN}) = 0$
$R_B = 10 \text{kN}$

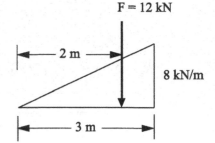

THE CORRECT ANSWER IS: C

51. Refer to Plane Truss: Method of Sections in the Statics section of the *FE Reference Handbook*.

Place a hypothetical cut as shown below, exposing Member BC as an external force. Then sum the moments about the point so the F_{BC} provides the only unknown moment.

$$\sum M_I = 0$$

$$\sum M_I = (5F_{BC}) - (5 \times 3) - (10 \times 3) - (15 \times 3) = 0$$

$$0 = 5F_{BC} - 15 - 30 - 45$$

$$F_{BC} = 3 + 6 + 9$$

$$F_{BC} = 18 \text{ kips}$$

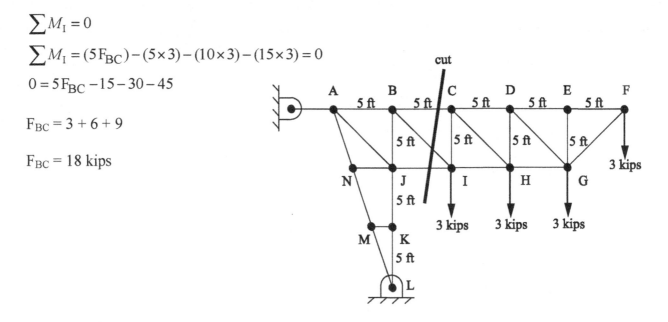

THE CORRECT ANSWER IS: D

FE OTHER DISCIPLINES SOLUTIONS

52.

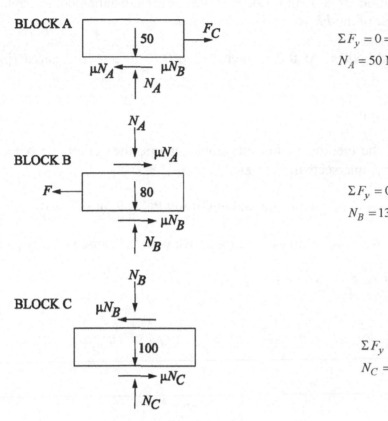

BLOCK A

$\Sigma F_y = 0 = -50 + N_A$

$N_A = 50 \text{ N}$

BLOCK B

$\Sigma F_y = 0 = -50 - 80 + N_B$

$N_B = 130 \text{ N}$

BLOCK C

$\Sigma F_y = 0 = -130 - 100 + N_C$

$N_C = 230 \text{ N}$

Assume Blocks A and C remain stationary.

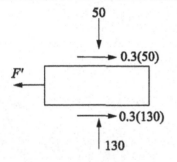

$\Sigma F_x = 0 = -F' + 0.3(50) + 0.3(130)$

$F' = 54 \text{ N}$

Assume Blocks B and C move.

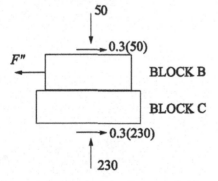

$\Sigma F_x = 0 = -F'' + 0.3(50) + 0.3(230)$

$F'' = 84 \text{ N}$

$\therefore F = 54 \text{ N}$ where A and C remain stationary.

THE CORRECT ANSWER IS: B

53. Refer to the section Plane Motion of a Rigid Body—Kinematics (Instantaneous Center of Rotation) in the Dynamics chapter of the *FE Reference Handbook*.

The crank and rod are two rigid bodies. At the moment when $\theta = 90°$, v_P is desired (piston speed).

$v_C = 50 \text{ mm} \times 377 \text{ rad/s} = 18{,}850 \text{ mm/s}$

Both points are on the rod. By the method of instantaneous centers, the center of rotation is located where the line at P, $\perp$ to v_P, intersects the line at C, $\perp$ to v_C.

v_C is parallel to v_P so these meet at infinity. Thus the rotation of rod PC is 0, or $\omega_{PC} = 0$.

Since there is no rotation at this instant, *all* points of the rod move with the same velocity and

$v_P = v_C = 18{,}850 \text{ mm/s}$ because $\bar{v}_P = \bar{v}_C + \bar{\omega}_{PC} \times \bar{r}_{P/C}$ and $\omega_{PC} = 0$.

THE CORRECT ANSWER IS: C

54.

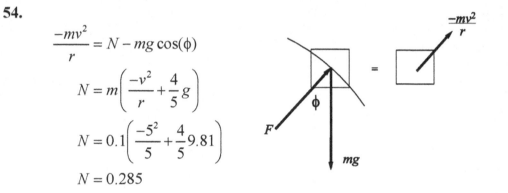

$$\frac{-mv^2}{r} = N - mg\cos(\phi)$$

$$N = m\left(\frac{-v^2}{r} + \frac{4}{5}g\right)$$

$$N = 0.1\left(\frac{-5^2}{5} + \frac{4}{5}9.81\right)$$

$$N = 0.285$$

THE CORRECT ANSWER IS: A

FE OTHER DISCIPLINES SOLUTIONS

55. First, the velocity is:
$$v = s' = 60t^2 - 4t^3$$

Then, the acceleration is:
$$a = s'' = 120t - 12t^2$$

Finally, the rate of change of acceleration is:
$$a' = s''' = 120 - 24t$$

When $t = 2$:
$$a' = 120 - 24(2) = 120 - 48 = 72$$

THE CORRECT ANSWER IS: A

56. Consider the bullet and both blocks as the "system." Write the momentum equation on the system with no external forces and with momentum conserved.

$$mass_b \times velocity_b = (mass_b + mass_B) V_B + mass_A \times V_A$$

$velocity_b = 500$ m/sec
$mass_b =$ mass of bullet, unknown
$mass_B =$ mass of Block B $= 2.5$ kg
$mass_A =$ mass of Block A $= 3$ kg
$V_A =$ velocity of Block A $= 3$ m/sec
$V_B =$ velocity of Block B $= 5$ m/sec

$$mass_b = \frac{mass_B \times V_B + mass_A V_A}{velocity_b - V_B} = 43.4 \text{ g}$$

THE CORRECT ANSWER IS: A

95

FE OTHER DISCIPLINES SOLUTIONS

57.   Refer to the Work and Energy section in the Dynamics chapter of the *FE Reference Handbook*.

$$T_2 + U_2 = T_1 + U_1 + W_{1\rightarrow 2}, \qquad W_{1\rightarrow 2} = -Fx$$

$$\frac{1}{2}mv_2^2 = \frac{1}{2}mv_1^2 - \mu_k mgx$$

Cancel m to obtain $\rightarrow \dfrac{1}{2}(10)^2 = \dfrac{1}{2}v_1^2 - 0.2(9.81)(20)$

$$v_1 = 13.4 \text{ m/s}$$

$F = \mu_k mg$

THE CORRECT ANSWER IS: C

58.   The kinetic energy T, when the object is at Q, is:
$T = 1/2\ mv^2 = 1/2\,(1.5\,\text{kg})(2\,\text{m/s})^2 = 3\,\text{J}$

THE CORRECT ANSWER IS: B

59.   Refer to Torsion in the Mechanics of Materials section of the *FE Reference Handbook*.

$$\tau = \frac{T\rho}{J}$$
$\therefore \max \tau$ when $\rho = r$

THE CORRECT ANSWER IS: A

60. Refer to Cylindrical Pressure Vessel in the Mechanics of Materials section of the *FE Reference Handbook*.

The cylinder can be considered thin-walled if $t \leq \dfrac{1}{10} r_i$.

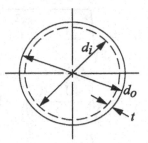

In this case,

$$d_i = 700 \text{ mm}$$
$$t = 12 \text{ mm}$$
$$d_o = d_i + 2t = 700 + 2(12) = 724 \text{ mm}$$
$$r_i = \frac{d_i}{2} = 350 \text{ mm}$$
$$r_o = \frac{d_o}{2} = 362 \text{ mm}$$

where $r = \dfrac{r_i + r_o}{2} = \dfrac{350 + 362}{2} = 356 \text{ mm}$

$$\sigma_t = \frac{P_i r}{t} = \frac{1.680 \text{ MPa} \times 356 \text{ mm}}{12 \text{ mm}} = 49.8 \text{ MPa}$$

THE CORRECT ANSWER IS: B

61. Rotating the plane 45° physically creates twice the angle on the Mohr's circle, resulting in a 90° Mohr's circle rotation. Thus, the correct answer is the center.

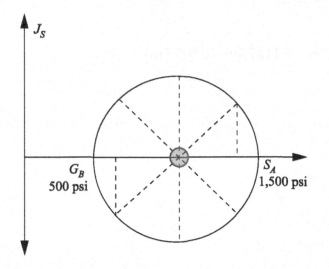

THE CORRECT ANSWER IS SHADED ABOVE.

62.   Refer to Mohr's Circle in the Mechanics of Material section of the *FE Reference Handbook*.

From a constructed Mohr's Circle, the maximum in-plane shear stress is $\tau_{max} = R$.

$$R = \sqrt{\left(\frac{\sigma_x - \sigma_y}{2}\right)^2 + \tau_{xy}^2}$$

$$R = \sqrt{\left(\frac{40 - 20}{2}\right)^2 + 10^2}$$

$$R = \sqrt{200}$$

$$R = 14.1 \text{ ksi}$$

THE CORRECT ANSWER IS: B

63.

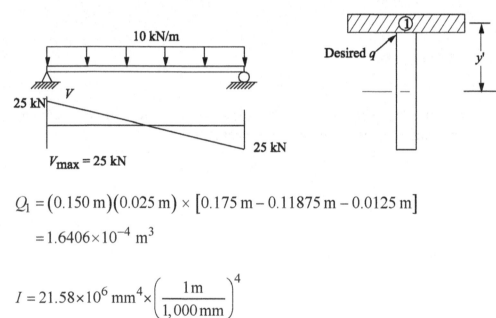

$$Q_1 = (0.150 \text{ m})(0.025 \text{ m}) \times [0.175 \text{ m} - 0.11875 \text{ m} - 0.0125 \text{ m}]$$

$$= 1.6406 \times 10^{-4} \text{ m}^3$$

$$I = 21.58 \times 10^6 \text{ mm}^4 \times \left(\frac{1 \text{ m}}{1{,}000 \text{ mm}}\right)^4$$

$$= 0.00002158 \text{ m}^4$$

$$q = \frac{VQ}{I} = \frac{25{,}000 \text{ N}\left[1.6406 \times 10^{-4} \text{ m}^3\right]}{0.00002158 \text{ m}^4}$$

$$= 190{,}060 \text{ N/m}$$

$$= 190 \text{ kN/m}$$

THE CORRECT ANSWER IS: B

64.

$$\frac{10\ \text{m}}{10\ \text{kN}} = \frac{x}{6\ \text{kN}}$$

$x = 6\ \text{m}$

Area 1 $= 13(2)$ $= 26\ \text{kN·m}$

Area 2 $= \dfrac{6(6)}{2}$ $= 18\ \text{kN·m}$

Area 3 $= 4(4)$ $= 16\ \text{kN·m}$

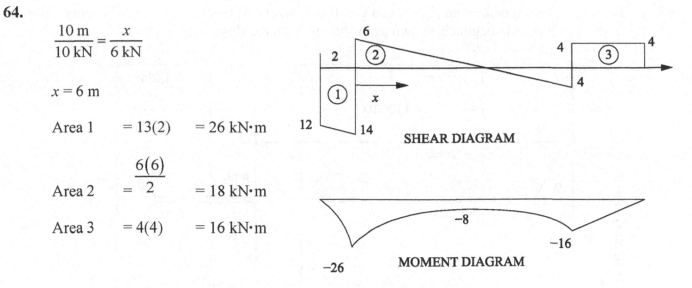

Maximum magnitude of the bending moment is 26 kN·m.

THE CORRECT ANSWER IS: D

65. Refer to the Mechanics of Materials section of the *FE Reference Handbook.*

$$\delta = \frac{5w_0\,L^4}{384\,EI} = \frac{5(10,000\ \text{N/m})(5\ \text{m})^4}{384(200 \times 10^9\ \text{Pa})(21.58 \times 10^{-6}\ \text{m}^4)} = 0.0189 = 18.9\ \text{mm}$$

THE CORRECT ANSWER IS: D

66. Refer to the Mechanics of Materials section of the *FE Reference Handbook.*

$$\nu = -\frac{\text{lateral strain}}{\text{longitudinal strain}} = -\frac{\varepsilon_r}{\varepsilon_x}$$

$$\text{lateral strain} = \varepsilon_r = \frac{-0.012\ \text{mm}}{20\ \text{mm}} = -0.0006$$

$$\text{longitudinal strain} = \varepsilon_x = \frac{0.2\ \text{mm}}{100\ \text{mm}} = 0.002$$

$$\nu = -\frac{-0.0006}{0.002} = +\,0.30$$

THE CORRECT ANSWER IS: D

FE OTHER DISCIPLINES SOLUTIONS

67. The solidification path of an Ag-70 w/o Cu alloy is shown as the vertical line. The temperature at which solidification begins is shown as the horizontal dashed line and is 920°C.

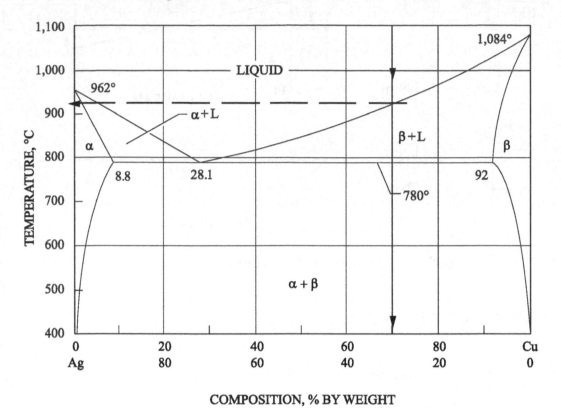

COMPOSITION, % BY WEIGHT

THE CORRECT ANSWER IS: B

68. Cold-working metal decreases the recrystallization temperature, ductility, and slipping or twining takes place. During cold work, grains become elongated instead of equiaxed.

THE CORRECT ANSWER IS: C

69. Aluminum is anodic relative to copper and, therefore, will corrode to protect the copper.

THE CORRECT ANSWER IS: B

70. Since strains are equal, $\varepsilon_f = \varepsilon_m = \varepsilon$.

The load borne by the fibers is $\sigma_f A_f = E_f \varepsilon A_f$.

The load borne by the matrix is $\sigma_m A_m = E_m \varepsilon A_m$.

The volume fraction and area fractions are equal.

The total load supported by the composite is the sum of the load supported by fiber and matrix = $E_m \varepsilon A_m + E_f \varepsilon A_f$.

The ratio is thus $\dfrac{E_f A_f}{E_f A_f + E_m A_m} = \dfrac{(70\,\text{GPa})(0.6)}{(70\,\text{GPa})(0.6) + (5\,\text{GPa})(0.4)} = 95.4\%$

THE CORRECT ANSWER IS: D

71. By definition, amorphous materials do not have a crystal structure.

THE CORRECT ANSWER IS: D

72. Material A is the most ductile, having the highest strain prior to fracture. Yield stress is measured at 0.2% strain. So the indicated point will be the yield stress of the most ductile material.

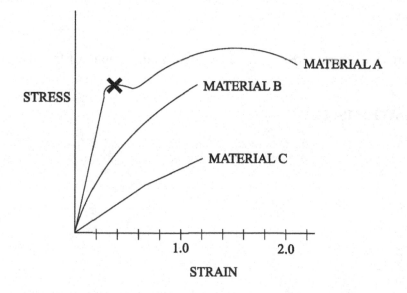

THE CORRECT ANSWER IS MARKED WITH AN X ABOVE.

FE OTHER DISCIPLINES SOLUTIONS

73. The equation can be found in the Fluid Mechanics section of the *FE Reference Handbook*. The shear stress τ is given by

$\delta = 0.25$ mm   OIL FILM   0.15 m/s

$$\tau = \mu \frac{dv}{dy}$$

The velocity gradient is uniform, so that

$$\frac{dv}{dy} = \frac{V_{top}}{\delta}$$

$$\tau = \frac{\mu V_{top}}{\delta} = \frac{\left(40 \times 10^{-3} \text{ N·s/m}^2\right)(0.15 \text{ m/s})}{0.00025 \text{ m}} = 24 \text{ Pa}$$

THE CORRECT ANSWER IS: C

74. Dye injected into laminar flow creates a straight line. Dye injected into turbulent flow disperses throughout the flow within a short distance. Therefore, A is not correct.

Laminar flow has R_e values below 2,000. Between 2,000 and 3,000, the flow is transitional. About 3,000, the flow is turbulent. Therefore, D is not correct.

Head loss is $h_L = f \times \dfrac{L}{D} \times \dfrac{V^2}{2g}$

Therefore, from this equation, energy loss varies directly with the square of the velocity.

THE CORRECT ANSWER IS: C

75.   The mean pressure of the fluid acting on the gate is evaluated at the mean height, and the center of pressure is 2/3 of the height from the top; thus, the total force of the fluid is:

$$F_f = \rho g \frac{H}{2}(H)(W) = 1,600(9.807)\frac{3}{2}(3)(1) = 70,610 \frac{\text{kg·m}}{s^2} = 70,610 \text{ N}$$

and its point of application is 1.00 m above the hinge. A moment balance about the hinge gives:

$$F(3) - F_f(1) = 0$$

$$F = \frac{F_f}{3} = \frac{70,610}{3} = 23,537 \text{ N} = 23.5 \text{ kN}$$

THE CORRECT ANSWER IS: C

76.   Volume flow rate = (cross-sectional area)(velocity)
$Q = Av$

$$A = \frac{\pi(0.06 \text{ m})^2}{4}$$

$$= 0.00283 \text{ m}^2$$

Energy equation (Bernoulli equation)

$$\frac{p_1}{\gamma} + \frac{v_1^2}{2g} + z_1 = \frac{p_2}{\gamma} + \frac{v_2^2}{2g} + z_2 + h_{f(1 \text{ to } 2)}$$

$p_1 = p_2 = 0$ psi: (gage) - open to atmosphere

$v_2 \approx 0$ m/s assumed negligible - large reservoir

$h_{f(1 \text{ to } 2)} = 0$ neglect friction loss

$$v_1 = \sqrt{2g(z_2 - z_1)}$$

$$= \sqrt{2(9.81 \text{ m/s}^2)(10 - 3)\text{m}}$$

$$= 11.7 \text{ m/s}$$

$$Q = (0.00283 \text{ m}^2)(11.7 \text{ m/s})$$

$$= 0.033 \text{ m}^3/\text{s}$$

THE CORRECT ANSWER IS: C

FE OTHER DISCIPLINES SOLUTIONS

77. Viscosity = μ = dynamic viscosity

$$(1.05\text{ cP})\left(0.001\frac{\text{Pa}\cdot\text{s}}{\text{cP}}\right)\left(\frac{\text{N/m}^2}{\text{Pa}}\right)\left(\frac{\text{kg}\cdot\text{m/s}^2}{\text{N}}\right)\left(\frac{1{,}000\text{ g}}{\text{kg}}\right)$$

so $1.05\text{ cP} = 1.05\text{ g/(m}\cdot\text{s)}$

$$\rho = 1.00\frac{\text{g}}{\text{mL}} \times \frac{1{,}000\text{ mL}}{1\text{ L}} \times \frac{1{,}000\text{ L}}{\text{m}^3} = 1 \times 10^6\frac{\text{g}}{\text{m}^3}$$

$V = Q/A$

$$\text{Area} = \pi\left(\frac{0.0525}{2}\right)^2 = 0.00216\text{ m}^2$$

$$V = \left(0.500\frac{\text{m}^3}{\text{min}}\right)\left(\frac{\text{min}}{60\text{ s}}\right)\left(\frac{1}{0.00216\text{ m}^2}\right) = 3.86\text{ m/s}$$

$\text{Re} = VD\rho/\mu$

$$\text{Re} = \left(3.86\frac{\text{m}}{\text{s}}\right)(0.0525\text{ m})\left(1\times10^6\frac{\text{g}}{\text{m}^3}\right)\Big/\left(\frac{\text{mgs}}{1.05\text{ g}}\right) = 1.93\times10^5$$

THE CORRECT ANSWER IS: C

78. $P = \gamma h$

$$= (9{,}800\text{ N/m}^3)(9\text{ m}) = 88{,}200\text{ N/m}^2$$

$$= 88{,}200\frac{\text{N}}{\text{m}^2}\frac{\text{Pa}\cdot\text{m}^2}{\text{N}} = 88{,}200\text{ Pa}$$

$$= 88.2\text{ kPa}$$

THE CORRECT ANSWER IS: C

79. From the Moody (Stanton) diagram in the Fluid Mechanics section of the *FE Reference Handbook*, with $\frac{\varepsilon}{D} = 0.0005$ and $\text{Re} = 2 \times 10^5$, f is 0.019.

THE CORRECT ANSWER IS: B

80.
$$\frac{\rho v^2}{2} = gh(\rho - \rho_{air})$$

$$\therefore h = \frac{\rho v^2}{2g(\rho - \rho_{air})} \approx \frac{v^2}{2g} \approx \frac{(2)^2}{(2)(9.8)} \approx 0.204 \text{ m}$$

THE CORRECT ANSWER IS: D

81. Make the following assumptions:

    (1) rigid-walled cylinder, 30 L in volume
    (2) initial state of air in the cylinder: 10 MPa, 600 K
    (3) final state of air in the cylinder: ? MPa, 300 K

Volume of gas and number of moles of gas are fixed.

Initially, at 10 MPa, 600 K, $v = 0.018 \text{ m}^3/\text{kg}$

Final state: $v = 0.018 \text{ m}^3/\text{kg}$, $T = 300 \text{ K}$
Interpolate between 4 and 6 MPa in table.

P is proportional to $1/v$

$$P = 4 + 2 \frac{0.018 - 0.0214}{0.0142 - 0.0214}$$

$$P = 4 + 2 \frac{(-0.0034)}{(-0.0072)}$$

$$P = 4.94 \text{ MPa}$$

THE CORRECT ANSWER IS: B

82. Refer to the First Law of Thermodynamics section of the *FE Reference Handbook* for special cases of closed systems and Charles' Law.

$w_b = P\Delta v$
$w_b = 100 \text{ kPa} (1,000 \text{ L} - 500 \text{ L})$
$w_b = 50,000 \text{ J}$
$w_b = 50 \text{ kJ}$

THE CORRECT ANSWER IS: C

83.

$$Q = W = 0$$

$$h_1 + \frac{V_1^2}{2} = h_2 + \frac{V_2^2}{2}$$

$$h_2 - h_1 = C_p (T_2 - T_1) = \frac{V_1^2 - V_2^2}{2}$$

$$T_2 = T_1 + \frac{V_1^2 - V_2^2}{2C_p} = 300 \text{ K} + \frac{(150 \text{ m/s})^2 - (50 \text{ m/s})^2}{2[1{,}000 \text{ J/(kg} \cdot \text{K)}]} = 310 \text{ K}$$

THE CORRECT ANSWER IS: C

84. Refer to the pump power equation in the Fluid Mechanics chapter of the *FE Reference Handbook*.

$$\dot{W} = \frac{Q\gamma h}{\eta} = \frac{\Delta P \cdot Q}{\eta} \qquad \text{since } \Delta P = \gamma h$$

$$\eta = \frac{\Delta P \cdot Q}{\dot{W}} = \frac{(0.9 \text{ kPa})(3.0 \text{ m}^3/\text{s})}{4.0 \text{ kW}} \cdot \frac{\left(\frac{\text{kN}}{\text{m}^2}\right) \times \left(\frac{\text{m}^3}{\text{s}}\right)}{\left(\frac{\text{kN} \cdot \text{m}}{\text{s}}\right)}$$

$$= 0.675$$

THE CORRECT ANSWER IS: C

85. **THE CORRECT ANSWER IS: C**

86. Before switching

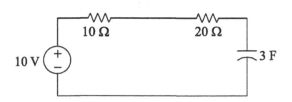

$$\tau = RC = (30)(3) = 90 \text{ s}$$

THE CORRECT ANSWER IS: A

FE OTHER DISCIPLINES SOLUTIONS

87. $R_T = 4\ \Omega + 3\ \Omega \| 6\ \Omega = 4\ \Omega + 2\ \Omega$

$R_T = 6\ \Omega \Rightarrow I_T = \dfrac{6\ \text{V}}{6\ \Omega} = 1\ \text{A}$

$I_x = \dfrac{3}{9}(I_T) = \dfrac{1}{3}\ \text{A}$

THE CORRECT ANSWER IS: A

88. Node 1: $\dfrac{V_1 - 100}{10} + \dfrac{V_1}{20} + \dfrac{V_1 - V_2}{30} = 0$

$11 V_1 - 2 V_2 = 600$

Node 2: $\dfrac{V_2 - V_1}{30} + \dfrac{V_2}{40} = 0$

$-4 V_1 + 7 V_2 = 0$

Solving, $V_1 = \dfrac{7}{4} V_2$

$11\left(\dfrac{7}{4} V_2\right) - 2 V_2 = 600 \Rightarrow V_2 = 34.78\ \text{V}$

THE CORRECT ANSWER IS: B

89. $Z = 30 + j90 - j50 = 30 + j40\ \Omega$

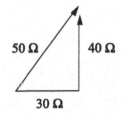

THE CORRECT ANSWER IS: D

90. S = apparent power
P = real power
Q = reactive power

$S = P + jQ = |S| \cos \theta + j\,|S| \sin \theta$

$\cos \theta = pf = 0.866$

$Q = (1{,}500\ \text{VA}) \sin[\cos^{-1}0.866] = 750\ \text{VAR}$

THE CORRECT ANSWER IS: B

91. The equation for pump work is:

$$W_P = \frac{v\Delta P}{\eta}$$

Refer to the Mechanical Engineering section of the *FE Reference Handbook*.

Assume $\eta = 1$.

$$W_P = 0.001017\ \text{m}^3/\text{kg} \times (4{,}140 - 27.6)\ \text{kPa/m}^2 = 4.183\ \text{kJ/kg}$$

THE CORRECT ANSWER IS: D

92. Flow through an insulated valve closely follows a throttling process. A throttling process is at constant enthalpy.

THE CORRECT ANSWER IS: D

93.

$$T_3 = T_1 = 275\ \text{K}$$

$$T_2 = T_1\left(\frac{P_2}{P_1}\right)\left(\frac{V_2}{V_1}\right) = 275\left(\frac{3{,}500}{3{,}500}\right)\left(\frac{1}{0.5}\right) = 550\ \text{K}$$

$$\dot{Q}_{23} = U_3 - U_2 = mC_v\left(T_1 - T_2\right) = \frac{P_2 V_2}{RT_2}C_v\left(T_1 - T_2\right)$$

$$= \left[\frac{3{,}500\ \text{kPa}}{0.287\ \text{kJ}/(\text{kg}\cdot\text{K})(550\ \text{K})}\right] \times 1\,\text{m}^3 \times \left[0.718\ \text{kJ}/(\text{kg}\cdot\text{K})\right](275 - 550)\text{K} \times \frac{1\ \text{kJ}}{1\ \text{kPa}\cdot\text{m}^3}$$

$$= -4{,}378\ \text{kJ}$$

THE CORRECT ANSWER IS: B

94. Isothermal process: $PV = mRT$
$P_2 V_2 = P_3 V_3$

$$V_3 = \frac{P_2 V_2}{P_3}$$

Also, $\Delta U = 0$ for isothermal processes $Q - W = 0$

$$_3Q_2 = \int_2^3 \delta Q = \int_2^3 PdV = mRT_1 \ln\frac{V_3}{V_2} = P_2 V_2 \ln\frac{V_3}{V_2}$$

$$\ln\frac{V_3}{V_2} = \frac{(60)(1{,}000)}{P_2 V_2}$$

$$= \frac{60{,}000}{(9\times10^5)(0.3)} = \frac{0.6}{2.7} = 0.2222$$

$$\frac{V_3}{V_2} = e^{0.2222} = 1.2488$$

$$V_3 = (0.3)(1.2488) = 0.375\,\text{m}^3$$

THE CORRECT ANSWER IS: A

95. Refer to the Heat Transfer section of the *FE Reference Handbook*.

$$\dot{Q} = hA\Delta T$$

$$\dot{Q} = 72(2)(150)$$

$$\dot{Q} = 21,600 \text{ W}$$

THE CORRECT ANSWER IS: D

96. As vapor escapes, the mass within the tank is reduced. With constant volume, the specific volume within the tank must increase. This can happen only if liquid evaporates.

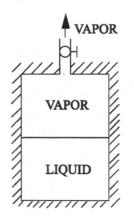

THE CORRECT ANSWER IS: A

97.

$$P_1 = 1 \text{ atm}$$

$$V_1 = 5 \text{ L} \qquad R = 0.082 \text{ L·atm} / (\text{mol·K})$$

$$T_1 = 300 \text{ K}$$

$$P_2 = 2 \text{ atm}$$

$$T_2 = 373 \text{ K}$$

$$V_2 = V_1 \left(\frac{T_2}{T_1}\right)\left(\frac{P_1}{P_2}\right) = 5\left(\frac{373}{300}\right)\left(\frac{1}{2}\right) = 3.108 \text{ L}$$

THE CORRECT ANSWER IS: A

98. $\Delta U = Q - W$

$= 2,000 \text{ J} + 4,000 \text{ J} = 6,000 \text{ J}$

$= m \, C \, \Delta T$

$= 15 \text{ kg} \times 4.18 \text{ kJ/(kg·°C)} \times \Delta T$

$$\frac{6,000 \text{ J}}{15 \text{ kg} \times 4.18 \dfrac{\text{kJ}}{\text{kg·°C}}} \times \frac{1 \text{ kJ}}{1,000 \text{ J}} = \Delta T$$

$\Delta T = 0.096°C$

THE CORRECT ANSWER IS: C

99. Refer to the Thermodynamics section of the *FE Reference Handbook.*

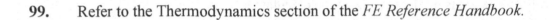

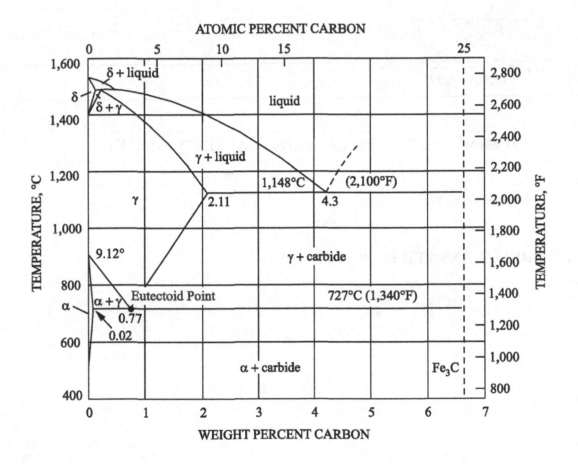

ATOMIC PERCENT CARBON

THE CORRECT ANSWER IS: A

100. When fouling occurs in a heat exchanger, the overall heat-transfer coefficient is given by the following equation from the Heat Transfer section of the *FE Reference Handbook*.

$$\frac{1}{U_o A_o} = \frac{1}{h_i A_i} + \frac{R_{(f)(i)}}{A_i} + \frac{\ln\frac{D_o}{D_i}}{2\pi k L} + \frac{R_{(f)(o)}}{A_o} + \frac{1}{h_o A_o}$$

The two fouling terms cannot be determined separately, and they will be combined into the following:

$$\frac{R_f}{A_o} = \frac{R_{(f)(i)}}{A_i} + \frac{R_{(f)(o)}}{A_o}$$

When the tube-wall resistance is neglected, R_f can be calculated.

$$\frac{1}{U_o} = \frac{A_o}{h_i A_i} + R_f + \frac{1}{h_o}$$

$$R_f = \frac{1}{U_o} - \frac{D_o}{h_i D_i} - \frac{1}{h_o}$$

$$= \frac{1}{700 \text{ W/(m}^2\cdot\text{K})} - \frac{25 \text{ mm}}{\left[2{,}500 \text{ W/(m}^2\cdot\text{K})\right](19 \text{ mm})} - \frac{1}{1{,}500 \text{ W/(m}^2\cdot\text{K})}$$

$$= 0.00024 \text{ m}^2\cdot\text{K/W}$$

THE CORRECT ANSWER IS: B

FE EXAM PREPARATION MATERIAL
PUBLISHED BY NCEES

FE Reference Handbook

FE Practice Exams for all modules:
Chemical
Civil
Electrical and Computer
Environmental
Industrial and Systems
Mechanical
Other Disciplines

For more information about these and other NCEES publications and services,
visit us at www.ncees.org or contact
Client Services at (800) 250-3196.